# "What Are You Offering?"

she demanded.

"A chance for us to discover each other."

Her throat closed. "A few weeks of fun and games?"

"Yes, that might be all there is." He took her swiftly in his arms. "Or there might be much more." His voice thickened possessively. "Much, much more.

Her lips trembling beneath his, she murmured, "I'm to gamble, is that it?"

"We'll both be gambling," he reminded her.

In spite of her doubts, she gave him her lips again and allowed herself to be swept along by desire as they clung feverishly to each other. This is it, she thought . . . this is love . . . when the bitter and sweet mingle. . . .

---

**MARY CARROLL**
is an internationally known American writer who has published both here and abroad. She brings to her romantic fiction a varied background of teaching and traveling that gives her a unique insight into the world of romance.

Dear Reader:

Silhouette has always tried to give you exactly what you want. When you asked for increased realism, deeper characterization and greater length, we brought you Silhouette Special Editions. When you asked for increased sensuality, we brought you Silhouette Desire. Now you ask for books with the length and depth of Special Editions, the sensuality of Desire, but with something else besides, something that no one else offers. Now we bring you SILHOUETTE INTIMATE MOMENTS, true romance novels, longer than the usual, with all the depth that length requires. More sensuous than the usual, with characters whose maturity matches that sensuality. Books with the ingredient no one else has tapped: excitement.

There is an electricity between two people in love that makes everything they do magic, larger than life—and this is what we bring you in SILHOUETTE INTIMATE MOMENTS. Look for them this May, wherever you buy books.

These books are for the woman who wants more than she has ever had before. These books are for you. As always, we look forward to your comments and suggestions. You can write to me at the address below:

Karen Solem
Editor-in-Chief
Silhouette Books
P.O. Box 769
New York, N.Y. 10019

# MARY CARROLL
# Two Faces of Love

*Silhouette* *Romance*
Published by Silhouette Books New York
**America's Publisher of Contemporary Romance**

Other Silhouette Books by Mary Carroll

*Shadow and Sun*
*Too Swift the Morning*
*Divide the Wind*
*Take This Love*
*Midnight Sun*

 SILHOUETTE BOOKS, a Simon & Schuster Division of
GULF & WESTERN CORPORATION
1230 Avenue of the Americas, New York, N.Y. 10020

Distributed by Pocket Books

ISBN: 0-671-57222-9

First Silhouette Books printing May, 1983

10 9 8 7 6 5 4 3 2 1

Map by Ray Lundgren

America's Publisher of Contemporary Romance

Printed in the U.S.A.

# Two Faces of Love

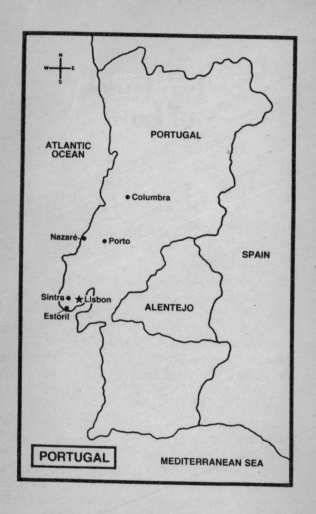

# Chapter One

"Ah, Claudio—thank you, my darling."

Isabel Alves, in shimmering purple, wrapped her shoulders in the shawl her escort held out, and then said in a voice ripe with melodrama, to Gina, "Prepare yourself, my dear American cousin. I am going to sing the fado now." Purple lids drooped over her black eyes. "You will hear the true heartbeat of Portugal for the first time."

Amused by Isabel, whom she was just beginning to know, Gina Thomas smiled across at Count Claudio Medoc, who was settling down again in his chair. She thought that the woman they were watching move into the spotlight was like some exquisite moth who showed her perfection only at midnight.

At the Alves's farm on the southern plains of Portugal where Gina had been visiting for the past few days, Isabel had tied back her black hair in a scarf and hat, protected her flawless skin with denims and long-sleeved shirts, and helped with the autumn harvest as zestfully as any man.

But here in the Alfama district of Lisbon where vivid posters in front of the Casa de Fado proclaimed Isabel "Queen of the *Fadistas,*" Gina had discovered another side of her—a sultry and sophisticated presence in her violet-hued satin with its plunging neckline.

Obviously Isabel was adored by the dozens of fans applauding at their tables, as well as by the handsome Italian count who had dogged her every step since her return earlier in the afternoon.

Isabel had her own apartment in Alfama and drove her own car—an expensive little sports coupé—and when her visit at the farm was over, she had insisted that Gina accompany her back to Lisbon.

"She will go mad here in the country with only you and Mama talking old times," Isabel complained when her father objected to parting with his niece so soon after her arrival. "She must go with me to the real Portugal. To where there is music and pathos."

Isabel's eyes had closed on that occasion, too, Gina recalled, and though her eyelids had been shadowed only by grime from the grain fields, still she had pleaded dramatically, "Gina must go where there is fado!"

Emilio's middle-aged face creased in pretended disgust. "Fado is all we hear these days." But he could not disguise how proud he was of the career his daughter had established for herself in the capital city, and he took her fondly on his knee as if she were still a dark-eyed girl of ten instead of a provocative beauty of twenty-four.

His wife, Valentina, who shared the sofa with him, also beamed her approval. Both appreciated the fine blend of Moorish fatalism and chivalric romance that characterized Portuguese culture and which was so well-expressed in the music of the fado; and like most of their countrymen, they held in high esteem the *fadistas,* the singers who preserve those melancholy fate songs that unfailingly deal with *suadade,* the longing for what might have been.

"In Lisbon," Valentina confided in a loud whisper, "there are perhaps one dozen *fadistas* of renown and of those, our Isabel ranks at the top."

Our Isabel, thought Gina, who watched with admiration as her cousin slithered to the bandstand, certainly had an impressive stage presence. The black shawl she had trailed after her when she entered the nightclub, now draped her shoulders, lending her the haunting appearance of a gorgeous young widow. Gina glanced again at Claudio, wondering a

little at his rapt look. He seemed too sophisticated to be taken in by such obvious dramat-
ics.

But within minutes Gina, too, was caught
up in the spell Isabel cast as the throbbing
lyrics of the fado permeated every corner of
the dimly lit room.

Only Isabel stood in light—a muted, irides-
cence that captured the soulful mood of her
songs and translated itself into flattering
shadows that blended magically with the hue
of her dress and with the color above her eyes.
When she was done after a quarter of an hour,
her audience sat gripped in silence; then re-
sounding applause, which Gina heartily
joined, shook the Casa de Fado.

Glancing around as the lights went up, Gina
was astonished to see how many people had
crowded into the tiny nightclub with its bull-
ring decor and provincial garlands of onions
and garlic strung behind the bar.

Gina was not unacquainted with the customs of her mother's homeland, and on Nantucket Island where she had grown up, a
strong Portuguese influence had fostered a
number of night spots similar to this one. She
had spent evenings there with her friends
soaking up atmosphere. But nothing in her
experience had prepared her for the authen-
ticity of the Casa de Fado.

Much of it, she realized slowly, derived
from the intensity of the people gathered
there. Isabel's songs seemed to have plunged
her listeners into a gloomy reverie, which

they obviously relished and had paid their money to indulge in. Where there was laughter, a deliberate sadness tinged it. Classically sculpted lips in swarthy faces smiled, but smiled pensively. And yet underlying it all, she observed, was an oddly cheerful air that was reflected in raised glasses and chairs tilted back companionably, and in the robust pleasure the men seemed to take in slapping each other across the shoulders and calling aloud one another's name.

The women, less demonstrative but no less melancholy, gazed languidly into their wine glasses and trailed slender fingers through their hair, all with the look of placid acceptance that life was cruel and sorrow inevitable —and that the combination was somehow quite delightful.

Observing Gina's absorption in her surroundings, Claudio Medoc took advantage of it to scrutinize her, his dark, close-set eyes intent on searching for the flaws he had missed earlier, but which his arrogant nature demanded he discover.

There was an air of remoteness about Isabel's cousin, an air of reserve that nagged at him the way an embedded thorn might. She was Isabel's age, he recalled, and yet she seemed older and annoyingly aloof.

She was too tall, he decided, and too thin— but he knew he was exaggerating. She was only slightly taller than Isabel, and though she was not as well endowed, enough roundness showed beneath the bodice of her fashionable silk dress to be enticing. Slim arms and elegant wrists completed the picture he saw across the table—except for the unexpected radiance that lit the space between them when she smiled.

She was a staggeringly attractive woman, he reluctantly concluded, and in a voice dolefully resigned, he said, "May I ask what you think of this place?"

Gina looked at him and thought that the melancholy songs of the fado had infected him, too.

"I think it's amazing, and so is Isabel." But almost at once she took her eyes away from his. Claudio Medoc was agreeable enough. One might even call him gallant with his studied air of Old World charm, but his good looks were too slick for Gina's tastes.

She mistrusted his shiny black hair, trimmed too perfectly, his chiseled features, and the paisley scarf twisted too smartly inside the collar of his white shirt.

Count Claudio Medoc did everything too effortlessly, like an arrogant maître d', who snapped his fingers and made tables appear where there was only air.

When she and Isabel had arrived at Isabel's apartment, Claudio had arrived almost simultaneously. One minute their bags were in the car, and the next, a dark-faced boy materialized at the flick of Claudio's wrist and lugged them up the stairs. Once they were in the apartment, Isabel sat down to fan herself on the couch and Claudio took command, raising shades and popping out ice cubes.

Gina repeated to Claudio over the roar of more applause for Isabel, "Absolutely amazing," but she thought: No more so than your being a part of Isabel's life, and she tried to imagine Claudio on the Alves's farm watching Isabel yoke the oxen.

Claudio took a cigarette from inside his jacket and tipped a flame to it. As if he had read her thoughts, he said, "What I like most about the Casa de Fado is its earthiness."

Gina bit back a smile, recalling another man like Claudio, a friend of Quentin Bromley's. Whenever he came to Nantucket to visit, he always insisted on being the one to gather the rockweed and dig the pit for the clambake so that afterward he could call to the attention of his New York friends his scratches and blisters.

Gina put down her wineglass and gazed around at the crowd. "Not all of these people appear to be part of the neighborhood."

Since Alfama was the most Moorish district remaining in cosmopolitan Lisbon, its inhabitants wore the marks of their centuries-long domination by the Arabs more distinctly than their compatriots.

"That couple over there, for instance." She nodded discreetly toward a man who had been staring at her and to the porcelain-skinned blonde who sat at the table with him.

Claudio's gaze slid over the pair. "There are

13

always outsiders who come to ogle," he said, and jabbed out his cigarette.

He seemed so annoyed, Gina could not resist asking, "Do you know them?"

"Oh, yes." He appeared to have bitten into a lemon. "The woman is Sylvia King. A widow. An American heiress." He let a disdainful look skip over Gina's questioning face. "And the man is Marcello Severa."

That seemed to be the end of it. Marcello Severa was either so well-known he needed no identification beyond his name, or else he did not merit any further attention from Count Claudio Medoc.

But Gina could not help stealing another glance at him. There was an arresting quality in the easy set of his wide shoulders and in the way he held his head to one side when the woman talked, as if he were listening with his whole person to everything she said, and not being taken in by any of it. He wore a white shirt, as Claudio did, but with the scarf folded into the open throat. Faded jeans stretched comfortably over his narrow hips and a pair of scuffed boots covered his feet.

His hair—she was dazzled by it—was thick and prematurely silver at the temples, and silvery again across the top of his head, but with more black showing through where it dipped down over one side of his forehead. His skin glowed as if his strong features and wide, engaging mouth were sculpted from copper. Set deep beneath heavy brows, his eyes, like coals, burned into the face of the woman opposite him.

He was thirty, Gina thought. Perhaps thirty-five. Unreasonably, she wished she were the woman to whom he was talking, and annoyed at herself, she took another sip of wine, intent on proving she could stop staring at him anytime she chose. But in a minute her gaze sought him again, and this time he was looking at her.

Isabel returned then, with her shawl over one shoulder and the swell of her breasts showing prominently above her low-cut neckline. Her cheeks were suffused with color that deepened as her body brushed between the tables and eager hands reached toward the whispering cloth of her dress and to her arms swinging past.

She took her seat with a queenly air that kept at bay even the most ardent of her admirers, but at the same time she gave off enough sparks to hold their worshipful attention.

"You were marvelous, Isabel," said Gina in genuine praise. "You had everyone in a trance."

"Naturally. That is Isabel's style." Claudio slid her hand between his own and stared down at it hungrily, as if he had created an irresistible sandwich he could hardly keep from biting into. "But you have only seen the beginning. Before the evening is over, she will sing twice more." His gaze shifted to make certain he held Gina's attention. "The crowd

15

will by hypnotized by then. She builds to a crescendo, you see."

"No, Claudio." Isabel appeared faintly bored. "Crescendo involves volume." To Gina, she said, "Fado is never loud."

Claudio's face hardened unpleasantly, and he took his hand away. "No, of course it isn't. That wasn't what I meant at all."

To soothe him, Isabel kissed him lightly on the lips and asked him to order her a glass of port. When he had turned away, her huge black eyes rested on Gina, and some of the natural enthusiasm she had exhibited at the farm broke through her languor. "So you were impressed, yes, by my singing? But you see, it is not so much my voice as it is the message the songs are carrying. Could you comprehend it?"

"The songs were all about love," said Gina, who had learned just enough Portuguese from her mother to get by in this land she was visiting for the first time. "About love and about losing it."

Isabel shrugged. "Like a coin, love has two faces. Rapture is one, sorrow is the other. It is not possible to separate them. In fado the bitter and the sweet mingle. That is life, and that is what I sing about." The purple eyelids came down. "I am moved by it myself."

Husky laughter sounded at Gina's elbow. "One day you will put yourself in a trance instead of your audience, Isabel, and then what shall we do for a queen of the *fadistas*?"

Isabel's eyes flew open. "Marcello! You are making fun of me," she said, "but you come often to hear me, I notice."

He was taller than Gina had imagined, more powerfully built, more commanding. But the attentive air was the same, except now that he was standing beside her she saw that his eyes were a dark blue, not black. When his glance fell on her, she felt as if he had touched her.

"Sit down, Marcello," Isabel invited, and then her voice cooled. "And Mrs. King, of course. Both of you must meet my dear American cousin. Claudio, drinks for everyone."

But Claudio was already producing drinks, lifting a bottle of amber port from the tray of a passing waiter and sending a swift glance toward another who came running with glasses. A convincing warmth rolled like butter off his tongue.

"Mrs. King, you look as beautiful as ever. You are staying through the winter I trust, or else we shall be desolate in Estoril."

Marcello Severa took a chair next to Gina, turning his remarkable eyes on her while Isabel made her introductions and then he murmured quietly, "You have chosen a good time to visit. Autumn in Portugal can be as beautiful—almost—as a woman."

Flustered, Gina answered, "Actually I didn't choose the season. It chose me." She realized she had barely nodded at Mrs. King, but Marcello Severa held her gaze. "I own a shop. I can leave only during the off-months when there aren't many tourists."

"What sort of shop?"

She moistened her lips. "Women's clothing."

"Did the dress you are wearing come from there?"

Gina felt as if he had opened the buttons of her silk bodice and run his hand inside. Now she did look at the woman Claudio had disdainfully referred to as an American heiress. Sylvia King, she said to herself, but she was thinking Marcello Severa. She was hearing the musical syllables chiming like bells in her head.

She knew he was still staring at her, but she made herself concentrate on what the King woman was saying. Something about Nantucket. Something about Quentin Bromley.

"I've heard your name," said Sylvia King. "You're Quentin Bromley's fiancée, aren't you?"

A moment followed when the whole Casa de Fado seemed to hold its breath with Gina. Then she said, "Not really. Not officially."

"Oh?" The arched eyebrows of Sylvia King rose above her patrician nose. "Quentin tells a different story."

"Quentin often exaggerates."

That wasn't true, of course. Quentin Bromley was the most factual man alive, every inch of him the lawyer whose word was unimpeachable, whose family had been practicing law on the island since the first whaling ship had left its harbor.

Gina had not accepted any of Quentin's numerous proposals of marriage, but she knew that he assumed she eventually would. She had done nothing to discourage that assumption and now—though she had put an ocean between them while she made up her mind—Quentin had aired his confidence that the engagement was a settled fact, and the word had reached Lisbon.

"Would you care to dance?"

Gina remembered where she was. "Is anyone else dancing?"

Marcello pushed back his chair. "Does it matter?"

He took her hand and led her to a dimly lit corner where tables had been shoved back and one of the guitarists, between sips of wine, was strumming softly on his instrument.

"Tell me, what is it like to live on Nantucket?"

They swayed to the music. Gina felt the warmth of Marcello's hand through the cloth of her dress and she imagined its imprint against her skin, copper-colored on her white flesh. . . .

She took a breath. "It's wonderful, especially now that the season is over and the island is quiet again . . . the calm before the winter surf begins to build. On the moors toward

Sconset the huckleberry is turning red, on the south shore the kites are flying."

"You sound as if you might be homesick. For Quentin Bromley?"

"I'm not. Not in the least."

He held her not so close that their bodies touched, but so that she smelled the enticing fragrance of his skin. Black hair tinged with silver showed where his shirt came together. "Were you upset by what Sylvia said?"

"Is that why you asked me to dance?"

"Partly. I'm not fond of inquisitions."

Gina smiled. "May I ask what you're conducting?"

He smiled, too, showing straight white teeth. "I was making a statement, not asking a question."

"Then it doesn't require an answer, does it?"

Beyond his shoulder she saw that everyone at their table was watching them. Claudio looked pleased, Isabel thought, her slender fingers toying with the ruffles at her neckline, and Sylvia King had no expression at all.

Gina said, "Do you live in Lisbon?"

She heard his low chuckle, but when she glanced up at him, she realized why he was amused. "I suppose since we don't know each other, we do have to ask questions, don't we?" Her usual poise faltered. "Well? Do you live in Lisbon?"

"I have an apartment here, but my home is in Sintra."

Gina recognized, from her mother's talk over the years, the name of that lovely resort spot to the north of the city. It was an old area, quiet and as yet uninvaded by wealthy transients on summer holidays. A feeling of satisfaction came over her. Sintra seemed the right setting for Marcello Severa—just as Estoril, the watering spot of exiles, was right for Sylvia King and Claudio Medoc. She relaxed a little in Marcello's arms.

"There's a marvelous castle at Sintra, isn't there?"

He chuckled again. "Not just one. But name a place in Portugal where there isn't a castle."

"I can't. I'm sorry. I've been here for only a few days—at Isabel's family farm in Alentejo," she explained, naming the prime farming region of the country. "Her father is my uncle. Do you know him and Valentina?"

"I know Emilio quite well. I've met Valentina."

From the coldness of his tone, Gina sensed that this was a subject best not pursued, and she made a mental note to ask Isabel why.

"It's odd," he commented when the music stopped, "that you and Sylvia should have a mutual friend."

Gina stiffened, disappointed that he had not been as sensitive as she in regard to what topics were acceptable for discussion and which were not, but she answered calmly, "I don't think it's especially odd. A number of

21

wealthy Easterners summer on Nantucket. The Bromleys have been there forever. Sylvia and Quentin were bound to meet."

He looked down at her. "But not you and Sylvia?"

She said, casually enough, she hoped, "Except when I go out with Quentin, I'm rarely involved in the social activities on the island —at least not with the summer crowd."

"Why not?"

For all her skill at sidestepping objectionable questions, Gina found it impossible not to give an answer to those depthless blue eyes.

"On Nantucket—as well as most other places in the world, I imagine—there are different classes. I'm a working girl. Women like Sylvia King come to the island to play."

"Sylvia remembered your name. How do you account for that?"

Why should I have to? she wondered, but again she complied without showing her annoyance. "My shop bears my name. I don't recall that Mrs. King has ever been a customer, but she probably has friends who have been."

"I see." All at once he was brisk. "Isabel is getting up to sing again. Shall we go back to the table?"

# Chapter Two

Isabel called from the bathroom where she was removing her make-up. "How did you like Marcello, my cousin?"

"Tell me about him," Gina countered. Dressed for bed ahead of Isabel, she leaned to look out the window, drinking in the silence of the narrow street below, devoid now of all activity, but still exuding the fragrance of its flowers banked in every doorway and spilling from every ledge in the early morning darkness.

Reluctantly, she brought her head back in. "Do you go out with him?"

Isabel emerged from the bathroom wearing a filmy nightgown that showed off her finely molded body, her high full breasts, her firm thighs. "It is with Claudio I go out now."

Did that mean that before Claudio there had been Marcello? That once they might have been lovers?

Gina was annoyed that the thought distressed her, and she turned her back on Isabel and began to rummage in her flight bag. "What sort of man is Marcello?"

Isabel reclined on the bed, sighing. "Marcello is exactly who he appears to be." Gina imagined that her eyelids, free of their purple shadow, were drooping nevertheless. "He is a man women pursue, a man one might think has only ten *escudos* when actually he has ten million."

Gina persuaded herself that this was what she wanted to know. "Where does his money come from?"

"Wineries in Douro, cork trees. Some of it is old family money. His father was very rich and he is the only heir. And once Marcello had farm land."

"But no more?" Gina turned around. Isabel looked lovely stretched out on the bed, her black hair framed by the pillow. No wonder Claudio could scarcely keep his hands off her. She was like a delicious ripe fruit begging to be picked. "What happened to his land?"

"It was taken away from him during the '74 revolution." Isabel yawned. "Marcello was what we call a *latifúndios*—a landlord who is, how do you say it?—absent. There were many such landlords. The revolutionaries took their property and divided it up among farmers who owned no land."

24

Gina bristled. "That hardly seems fair."

Isabel's voice held no rancor. "That is depending on which side is yours. If you have nothing, and you get something, you think it is very fair."

Gina admitted the logic of this, but she had another question. "Uncle Emilio, was he involved in the transfer of the land?"

Isabel shook her head. "Our farm is small to begin with. No one pays any attention to it. But Father approved the breaking up of the estates. Some of the *latifúndios*, they were like, what do you say? . . . vacuum cleaners, sucking up everything, calling it their own."

"I see. Shall I turn out the light?" Then lying beside Isabel in the dark, Gina commented, "I suppose that explains why Marcello was cool when I spoke of your father."

Isabel sat up and snapped the light back on. "What does Marcello say?" She was wide awake again. "You don't know how I suffer because of this disapproval, Gina! Marcello of Father, Father of Marcello."

*Then it was true—they had been lovers.* But in the next breath Isabel refuted that assumption. "I am sure that is what is keeping Marcello from me. You saw tonight we are friends. He always jokes with me. He likes my songs."

Isabel's large eyes welled with tears of frustration. "But he never kisses me, never makes love to me!" She folded her arms beneath her full breasts. "Instead he wastes his time with this white worm of a woman—this American!"

Seeing Gina's stunned look, Isabel realized too late how her words must sound to another American. With a cry, she dragged her cousin up from the bed and threw her arms around her.

"Oh, you must forgive me, my darling Gina! Until you came, all I knew of your country was Mrs. King, this lady I despise. Now I know you, and I see it is not America that is wrong, it is only this woman who has captured Marcello's heart. I only say these bad things because of her."

"I understand, Isabel." But Gina had scarcely noticed the *faux pas*. "Are you in love with Marcello?"

Isabel's face took on its *fadista* plaintiveness. "For a long time, but alas, Marcello is not in love with me."

Like the audience who had hung on every word of her songs, Isabel seemed to find pleasure in her misery. "For now, I must content myself with Claudio. I do not mind because he is amusing, he is handsome—and he is of royal blood." Plainly, that impressed her most of all. "But someday . . .," Isabel's sigh was heartfelt, yet she wore a smile, "someday, who knows? Someday Marcello may say to me, 'Isabel, my darling, I love you.'"

The sun was high and poking bright fingers into the canyonlike streets of the Alfama district when Gina woke at midmorning, but Isabel only stirred, turned on her side and slept again—not surprisingly, Gina thought, since the two of them had talked on after they had put out the light for the second time.

But for Gina, the sounds from beneath the apartment window were too intriguing to allow her to lie in bed once she was awake. Without disturbing Isabel, she dressed swiftly in a frilly denim shirt and corduroy jeans that matched the gray of her eyes. Then she went to lean a moment on the windowsill as she had done the evening before, observing with fascination the activity below.

A snakelike procession of black-clothed women balancing laundry baskets on their heads maneuvered the narrow passages between the tall tenements. Isabel's apartment was modern and luxurious, yet she could see that most of the quarter followed a modest, outdated lifestyle.

The shouts of children playing in the alleyways mingled with the murmuring voices of old people gossiping on door stoops as they tended smoking braziers. A wandering accordionist stopped long enough for a handout of grilled sardines, and then was on his way again. In a tiny courtyard, Gina glimpsed the brilliance of bougainvillaea and watched two women chatting as they filled their water jugs.

Eager to be down on the street observing more closely this fascinatingly different culture, Gina was glad she and Isabel had agreed that while she was in Lisbon she should be free to do as she pleased.

"You must follow the routine you're accustomed to," Gina had made Isabel promise the day before when they were nearing the city. "I'm flattered that you want to share your apartment with me, but I'm used to being alone, and I'll work out my own itinerary. Of course we'll meet whenever we want to, and naturally I want to come often to hear you sing, but you mustn't treat me as a guest."

She had a horror of always being underfoot, particularly after she met Claudio. Isabel seemed to understand and as soon as they were settled, she had drawn a rough map for her cousin.

Stuffing it into her pocket, Gina let herself out of the apartment, but halfway down the stairs, she ran into Claudio on his way up.

It was an awkward moment. Gina was certain he was accustomed to coming and going and staying as long as he liked whenever he pleased, and they both stared at each other, neither of them sure of how to get by it.

Then Claudio, in the gallant way that annoyed her, swung about and took her arm. "We must go and find some breakfast for you."

This was Gina's objective, but Claudio was the last person she would have chosen to share the meal with.

Polite protests were futile however. "Nonsense," he said in answer to all of her objections. "If Isabel is still asleep, of course I won't wake her. Besides, you might have difficulty finding a restaurant."

The café he chose was one Gina admitted she would have passed by since it had no sign, only a door opening onto a long, unlighted passageway, but at the end of it they came out into a courtyard ablaze with flowers. Half-a-dozen people were seated at tables covered with checkered table cloths, set with bright pottery dishes.

With only a word Claudio's command brought forth coffee and rolls and then he set himself to the task of being an amusing host. Gina was grateful for the tips he gave her on exploring the city, but when they were having their second cup of coffee, he said with an acuteness she shrank from, "You were terribly impressed with Marcello Severa last night, weren't you?"

Gina was relieved that he did not wait for an answer. "Women always are," he went on airily. "Even Isabel sometimes thinks she is struck with him." He gave a thin laugh. "Can you imagine the two of them together?"

Gina could, and wished herself anywhere but here, pinned on the mocking gaze of this devilish man. He was like some sharp-billed bird, she decided, prying under leaves and bark for whatever tasty, malevolent thing that might be hidden there.

"They are both handsome people," she told him, aware that she had not included him in her compliment. "I shouldn't think it unusual if they were attracted to each other."

"Oh, Marcello isn't attracted to Isabel. Surely you could see that." As if she were blind if she couldn't! "Isabel is too . . . ," His shoulders lifted in a shrug beneath his silk shirt, "too voluptuous."

Sexy was the more frequently used American term, but Gina liked the round sound of Claudio's word, for it fit Isabel perfectly, and she smiled more warmly.

"Is it your opinion that *senhor* Severa is not interested in voluptuousness?"

Claudio's polished veneer collapsed in a scowl that clearly said the conversation was taking a turn he hadn't intended. He said coldly, "He looks for it in those who are more skilled at concealing it than Isabel."

Meaning Sylvia King. Gina thought of the masked gaze the heiress had turned on Marcello and herself as they danced, and she kept silent. Claudio was shrewd. She had to give him credit for that even though she disliked him. Sylvia King's blondeness held the flawless perfection of a porcelain figurine, making it difficult to imagine her rigid beauty disturbed by passion, without seeing it at the same time cracked in pieces.

But Gina had not missed the possessive sultriness with which the heiress had taken hold of Marcello's arm when they excused themselves after Isabel's songs.

Claudio poured them each another cup of

coffee and took a different tack. "I was interested to learn that you are engaged. Bromley
—was that his name? Isabel failed to mention
that fact."

Gina brought her gaze around to his. "Perhaps that's because I hadn't mentioned it to
her." She spoke quietly but inwardly she
raged at the shrewd face across from her.
"Also, it is not a fact. It is a rumor picked up
somewhere by Mrs. King."

Where? Gina wondered all at once. Last
night she had been too stunned to be curious.
If Sylvia King had been in Portugal all summer, as the conversation at the table had
indicated, when had she spoken to Quentin?

With unfailing keenness, Claudio read her
thoughts. "At least it's a fairly recent rumor,
I'd say, since only last week Sylvia made a
quick dash to the States." Blue smoke from
his cigarette encircled his head. "Something
about stocks and bonds, I believe. Perhaps
your planes crossed in midair."

The stock exchange. Quentin had a seat
there, and he went frequently to New York.

The world was too small, Gina thought, and
suddenly she was so weary of Claudio Medoc
that she rose with her napkin still in her hand
and offered a brisk excuse for leaving him
before they had finished their coffee.

"I have some shopping to do."

Claudio's smile told her he wasn't fooled,
but obviously he had learned whatever he had
sought to find out and was ready to dismiss

her. Still smiling, he wished her a pleasant day. "Will we be meeting for dinner?"

Over her shoulder, Gina said, "I think not," and hurrying down the dark passageway, she hoped fervently that she could manufacture some excuse to stay at home when Isabel and Claudio left in the evening for the Casa de Fado.

She was still trying to puzzle out Claudio's motive for cross-examination about Quentin when she paused at the end of a winding street to gaze down at the River Tagus, which cut through the city.

The sight was breathtaking, and at once her mind cleared of everything except the pleasure produced by looking at the river. A graceful orange suspension bridge spanned the water. Below, the river traffic was heavy and varied, and on the opposite bank from where she stood, the renowned statue of Christ the King guarded the city, its arms outstretched.

Suddenly, she was aware of a resonant voice at her elbow. "A penny for your thoughts, *senhorita*."

Marcello Severa stood at her side. But how absurd! was Gina's first reaction. The meeting was too similar to the one the evening before when he had appeared unheralded at Claudio's table in the Casa de Fado. He even wore the same jeans—or a matching pair. But there was one difference. He wore a checkered shirt this time, with the top button open to reveal his thick neck and curling hair below it. There was another difference, too. She observed with a slight tremor: Sylvia King was not with him.

"Do you always come sneaking up on people?"

"Always—if I can. I like to catch them unaware." He slouched comfortably against the low wall over which she had been gazing. The sunlight played on his silver hair. "It enables me to know what they're thinking."

"Then you shouldn't have to offer pennies to find out."

The creases around his mouth deepened. "Yours is not a face that gives away much."

She held out her hand. "In that case, I'll take your penny, sir, and tell you that I was wishing my mother were here to see this view."

Instead of putting a coin in her hand, he studied her upturned palm for a moment and then let it go. "If your mother has never been to Lisbon, you must bring her here."

"My mother died in the summer."

"I'm sorry."

Gina drew a shaky breath, still feeling the warmth of his grasp. "But she was born only a short way from here. In Palma. When she was a young girl her father took his family and emigrated to Nantucket. Emilio stayed only until he was grown, but my mother married and settled there." Gina glanced toward the river again. "I'm sure when she left this country that bridge wasn't built. Nor the statue of Christ, either."

"The statue was not erected until after the Second World War." Marcello seemed to be memorizing her profile with his deep-set eyes. "How long a visit do you plan in Portugal?"

A shiver of excitement that was not entirely welcome rippled over Gina. Why did he want to know? Was he merely making conversation? "I have five more weeks. I've closed my shop, and the summer stock I've ordered won't start arriving until the first of December."

"What a pity you can't stay to see the almond trees bloom." Before she could ask where, he went on. "I am interested that you are a businesswoman." He said the word in a faintly disdainful way, his gaze touching her parted lips and then following the line of denim ruffles down into the shadow between her breasts. "I would have thought you were a woman who paints or one who follows another of the arts."

Gina bristled. Once she had hoped to study literature, but when one ran a shop with only incidental help, there was scarcely time even to read. "Perhaps I would have, if I'd had a college education."

She wondered afterward if the edge in her voice had cautioned him not to question her further, or if he had simply tired of the subject. At any rate, he said suddenly, "Do you know that I've been tracking you?"

Her face showed her surprise. "Why?"

"I woke up this morning and decided to take you on a picnic." He said it as casually as if they had been friends for years. "But when I went around to Isabel's, she was just getting up and you were gone. She didn't know where."

The attentiveness Gina had noticed the evening before was a kind of concentration, she decided, and she was dizzy looking at his blue eyes. He would have made an excellent hypnotist, she thought.

"I was out having breakfast."

He set his head to one side and a sparkle of amusement lit his copper face. "With Claudio. From a block away I saw you pop out of Ninfa's, and then Claudio a moment afterward, strolling along as though he owned the world."

"He isn't that sure of himself," Gina came back sharply, and then she felt her face turn hot. "That was unpleasant of me. I'm sorry."

"Don't be." Marcello's eyes had narrowed appreciatively. "You're an astute observer."

"He annoys me with his prying."

"And with his matchmaking, too, I would imagine." Marcello smiled mysteriously. "If he could see the two of us together, I suspect it would make his day."

Why? Gina wondered, surprised. Because Isabel was interested, too, in Marcello?

But Marcello left her no time to muse further. "Enough of Count Medoc, or we'll spoil our own day. Come along. Let's go and put together a lunch, and then we'll find a taxi and be on our way."

Gina hesitated. "Where are we going?" Her breathlessness amazed her. After all, she wasn't a schoolgirl! But a whole day with Marcello Severa? Should she say something to Isabel first? Should she go at all? What had Isabel thought when he had appeared asking for her?

Marcello took hold of her hand and pulled her along after him. "We're going to the Castelo de São Jorge—the Castle of St. George. Look. . . ."

He pointed beyond the roofs of the towering tenements, and she saw the ruins hanging above the city, turreted and awesome.

"How grand it looks!"

"It's grander inside the walls!" He seemed delighted with her enthusiasm and tucked an arm around her waist in a gesture so companionable she could hardly object. It said that they were friends, off for an outing.

Her radiant smile broke through her reserve. "I think I must have worn these clothes just because I knew you'd come along with a plan for a picnic."

"Of course. It was fated. I knew the moment I saw you sitting with Claudio last night that you and I could communicate."

Gina felt a chill of apprehension. Such a cold word, communicate. But it could have many meanings. . . .

A surge of joy welled up in her. The sky was

36

a smashing blue, the air was crystal. It was a morning made for happiness, and skipping to match her step with Marcello's, Gina decided that Fate truly had brought them together. Fate, then, could be responsible for what happened between them—for this one day at least.

# Chapter Three

The rickety taxi that wound its way up what appeared to be Lisbon's highest hill was shuddering and wheezing when it reached the summit, but the good-natured driver seemed unperturbed.

"Don't forget, *senhorita*," he called after Gina through the open window. "Look for a white peacock feather." Then he gave Marcello a wink, kissed his fingertips in a cavalier fashion, and roared off down the cobbled road.

Gina laughed. "What would I do with a white peacock feather? Wear it in my hair?"

"Wear it next to your heart." Gina saw the amusement in Marcello's eyes. "You might find that a bit uncomfortable, but young women in this part of the world do it all the time, symbolically at least. An ordinary feather from one of those vain birds is said to bring bad luck, but finding a white one means that the next man you see you will marry."

Gina could think of no response, but Marcello filled the silence, his gaze focusing with disturbing intensity on her lips. "Of course, since you are already engaged to be married, you would not be interested in this rather silly romantic custom."

It irked Gina to be reminded of Quentin Bromley twice in the space of an hour when she had crossed an ocean to avoid thinking about him, but just in time she realized if she protested too vehemently, that could be damaging, too.

With a bland smile she replied, "I think it's a charming custom, particularly since I didn't know white peacocks even existed."

"Perhaps they don't anywhere else." Marcello shouldered the picnic basket and started up the path leading toward the soft yellow battlements that appeared to be all that remained of the castle. "The ones found here are the descendants of an ancient line, though I'm afraid generally we simply accept them as part of the place without wondering if they have relatives elsewhere."

Over his shoulder he added with a sardonic lift of his lips, "But even if you were interested in discovering a feather from one of them, to do so would be highly unlikely. I'm told the villagers snatch them up the minute the birds shed them. They fetch a good price in the city."

"The villagers?" Gina turned from gazing at the panoramic view of Lisbon afforded by the height. "From Alfama, you mean?"

"No, there's a village inside the walls." He waited for her at the crest, and then taking her hand, he led her onto the castle grounds proper where there was not only a lovely park laid out in the area of the fortress that had preceded the castle, but a tiny village as well, complete with shops, a square, and a church all its own.

There was also a veritable menagerie loose on the grounds. Pink-kneed albino flamingos mingled with the snowy peacocks, and between the moats, Chinese pheasants strolled among skittering fantail doves. Everywhere Gina looked she saw either ducks, turkeys, swans, geese, or storks.

"This is fantastic!" she said to Marcello when he had selected a picnic table in a central spot where she could see everything all at once. "A zoo on top of a mountain!"

He laughed. "A rather casual zoo. I doubt if anyone would object if you decided to haul away half a dozen of these creatures."

"Who feeds them?"

Marcello held out a piece of cheese from the lunchbasket and at once an arrogant peacock shot forth and plucked it from his fingers.

"Quick!" said Gina in mock alarm. "Let's eat while we still have something left."

In a shop before they hailed their taxi, Marcello had purchased a bottle of dry white port for an apéritif, which he uncorked now and poured into pottery cups. For the main repast they helped themselves to thick slices of dark bread, the cheese the peacock found so appealing, and salted sardines.

When they had eaten and drunk their fill, Marcello brought out for dessert a bit of almond-flaked *gateau* that was too delicious for them to share even a crumb with an inquisitive raven perched above the table.

Feeling delightfully relaxed and content, Gina gazed at Marcello. "Thank you for bringing me here today. It's given me a wonderful introduction to Lisbon."

He looked at her from beneath half-lowered lids. "I thought perhaps Claudio had beat me to that."

"Claudio took me to breakfast—but only because Isabel was temporarily unavailable."

Marcello made no comment, and Gina thought less comfortably of Isabel's feelings for this compelling man who had so casually arranged her day for her. If her cousin had not confided in her, she might have more fully enjoyed the outing—but, she consoled herself, at least Claudio would be happy having Isabel all to himself.

"Tell me about your shop," said Marcello.

Gina remembered the faint derision with which he had mentioned it earlier. "I don't want to bore you."

"Why should I be bored?" He set his head to one side and looked at her in the way he had looked at Sylvia King the evening before. "I know nothing about women who run shops, so whatever you tell me will be fascinating."

If he were being facetious, he gave no hint of it in his expression or his voice, and she observed nothing condescending in his manner.

"I know nothing about women who run shops either," she replied. "I only know about one woman and one woman's specialty store." She paused a moment to decide if she should go on. "I try always to think of Gina's as being an entirely original concept so my patrons will adopt that attitude, too, and feel that they can't properly outfit themselves anywhere else."

"Who taught you to be so shrewd?" Marcello inquired.

Gina objected to his applying to her the term she herself had used to unflatteringly describe Claudio, but it was true that shrewdness—and more—had been necessary to rescue her source of livelihood from the brink of bankruptcy.

"My father taught me," she answered. "But not by example."

"Oh?" Marcello's interest quickened. "He wasn't the business success you are?"

"He was a washout," she replied calmly. "I served a long apprenticeship observing his mistakes. They were the most valuable lessons I could have learned anywhere."

"So now he sits back and congratulates

himself on his reverse psychology," Marcello commented, smiling.

"My father is dead. He died four years ago in a boating accident. Just in time, I might add."

She saw that she had shocked him, but she went on in the same unemotional tone. From the look on her face she might have been describing a casual acquaintance. "He was an excellent sailor, as he should have been since he spent most of his time on the water. But in spite of his skill, he allowed the boom of his sailboat to fracture his skull. He fell into the sea and drowned."

"That must have been terrible for you," Marcello murmured. "And for your mother."

"Actually it wasn't totally unexpected." Gina's look remained unchanged. "The accident was typical of the careless way he conducted his life. By the time he died, we were used to terrible things. But fortunately he hadn't gotten around to borrowing on his insurance policies so at least we had that much to start over with when he was gone."

Marcello's expression hardened. "Obviously there wasn't much love lost between you and your father."

In spite of her own frankness, Gina had not expected him to be blunt. A swift shaft of pain darkened her eyes.

Marcello saw it. "Am I being unfair?" he inquired in a softer tone.

"Inaccurate might be a better word." She looked away, letting him know that she was offering nothing more. What she had told him was public knowledge, but she had no intention of revealing to him or anyone else her private feelings about her father.

He waited a moment, and then he said, "After your father's death, you took over the shop?"

She wondered why he wanted to go on with this, but she nodded. "When he was managing it, we carried men's clothes, too, but when I took charge, my resources were limited, so I narrowed our stock to include only women's things. I gambled everything on the best designers. It was touch-and-go for awhile, but it finally worked out."

He looked directly at her. "And now you can afford trips to Portugal?"

She looked back at him. "Over my father's dead body. Is that what you're thinking?"

He said quietly, "It wouldn't have occurred to me that a mouth as soft-looking as yours could say hard things."

Gina flinched, but she answered evenly, "You might as well hear them from me as from Mrs. King."

"What makes you think Sylvia knows what you've told me?"

"If she doesn't now, she will soon." Gina lifted her chin. "She'll make it her business to find out."

A flicker of amusement burned briefly in Marcello's stare. "You don't miss much, do you?"

"It's a trait I've learned," she answered

coldly. "When one is sinking for the last time, one can't afford to overlook anything."

Marcello closed the lid on the picnic basket. "Shall we go for a walk?"

Moving along beside Marcello through the park, Gina reflected on what had passed between them. He had a different opinion of her now than he had held this morning when he came looking for her, and probably that was just as well.

If he considered her hard-hearted, he was right in a way. Too soft a heart could never have withstood Christian Thomas's careless treatment. Her mother's early death had been proof of that.

Yet Gina had never been able to hate her father. Her early memories of him were too vivid. She could not forget the laughter in his gray eyes, so like her own; or his arms swinging her above his head; or his lean, tanned body bending over her bed when he kissed her good night.

She hadn't known then that he was going out with a woman who wasn't his wife. She only knew how eagerly she had looked forward to the scent of his shaving lotion and his chin nuzzling against her neck.

My little queen, he had called her before he shortened her name from Regina. He could light up the darkest day with a word, a smile, or some special little joke he whispered in her ear.

But he never remembered her birthday. He

spent his Christmases somewhere else, splurging lavishly on presents that arrived late or giving her nothing at all. When she graduated from high school, he didn't know she was the valedictorian until he read it in the newspaper.

He was a philandering rascal, a spendthrift that her friends snickered about behind her back, but whom they loved to flirt with when he asked them to dance at the club. When Gina was sixteen, he spent her college money on a yacht and then took several friends sailing for two weeks in the Caribbean.

He was despicable, but by the time Gina was old enough to know it, it was too late to stop loving him. All she could do was freeze whenever he came near and remember for as long as she lived that handsome, sensuous men whose smiles could turn one's bones to jelly were never to be trusted.

She took a sideways look at Marcello. He was that sort of man. For a little while today she had forgotten that he was. He seemed so unaware of his charms, so disinterested in the power he could exert with a single smoldering glance, but that was part of the treachery of such men. They were beguiling magicians who could turn the stiffest backbone into a limp silk handkerchief and use it to wipe their shoes.

Let Marcello Severa think her cold. If he tried to defrost her, she would set him straight soon enough.

Marcello, however, seemed to have no interest in warming up Gina. He was aloof, if anything. He took her hand when he led her through the village, pointing out the ancient church and the little girls with lace handkerchiefs on their heads streaming out of its doors, but his touch was as impersonal as if she were one of them and he were an uncle entertaining her for the afternoon.

For an hour or so they wandered through the shops. Despite the hordes of tourists who had begun to pour out of taxicabs, he found an empty table in a tavern and bought her a glass of *verdalho,* a fruity sweet wine she had never tasted before. He told her funny stories of his childhood when he had hidden in the ruins of the castle and made his poor nurse almost go out of her mind chasing after him. The skin around his eyes crinkled with laughter when he described how he had once caught that same nurse kissing a guard when she thought Marcello was taking a nap.

Listening to him, Gina relaxed. He was fun to be with. There was no question of that. But she could feel the distance he kept between them in spite of his casual air, and though it made her oddly uneasy, she was glad of it.

She felt almost comradely toward him when they were walking back toward the table where they had left their picnic basket.

"What happened to you after you stopped wearing short pants?" she teased.

His gaze slid over her, and a faintly sardon-

47

ic smile lifted his lips. "I thought perhaps Isabel had told you that. Didn't you discuss me?"

He saw the spots of pink that appeared in her cheeks and said mildly, "Never mind. I don't object to filling in the blanks. My mother was Spanish," he began. "And my father was Portuguese—which is to say that war was declared in my blood before I was born."

Gina waited for him to go on, watching the play of light through the leaves as it speckled their path.

"We lived in Douro until I was ten. Then we moved to the family farm in the Alentejo region, and I spent the summers there and the winters in Sintra. While I was at the university in Coimbra, my father died. My mother returned to Madrid, and after I took my degree, I assumed the responsibilities of my family's interests."

"Cork," said Gina. "And wineries." She lifted her face to meet his glance. "Isabel did tell me that much. She said that you were . . ." She groped for the Portuguese word that she had forgotten and then gave up the effort. "You were an absentee landlord and lost your estate in the revolution. I wanted to know why you and my uncle aren't friends." Her gaze was frank.

"I admire Emilio," Marcello answered. "He's a good farmer." His jaw hardened. "But so was I. I didn't live on the land or till the soil, but I never reneged on my responsibility to my tenants. Fourteen families earned good

48

incomes on my estate. They shared in the profits. No one suffered."

He stopped beside the picnic table and waved at a band of screaming peacocks that had settled around the wicker basket that held the remains of their lunch. "Someday I'll show you the state of my land now and the lives those who farm it are leading. You can judge for yourself whether it is better to have freedom . . ." He gave the word a bitter twist. "Or to have someone in charge who is capable of directing men who have no idea how to proceed on their own."

"Emilio's farm is thriving," Gina said.

"It was thriving before the revolution," Marcello replied. "He is enterprising, capable, and fortunate. His farm is not too large for him to manage alone and too small for the revolutionaries to be interested in. After the uprising he had no adjustment to make, his land did not change hands. While his neighbors were recovering from the shock of independence, he was planting and harvesting his crops. While the revolutionary drum was beating, he never missed a step. Of course he is thriving."

Gina had noticed Emilio's cockiness, but he was still her uncle. Marcello was almost a stranger. She turned toward the picnic basket to signal that she was putting an end to the day as well as to the conversation, and then she drew back in dismay.

"Look at what those wretched birds have done! They've torn the top off and pecked

holes in every side to get at the cheese. Shoo!"
she cried as one strutting white fowl bobbed
its head at her.

Marcello laughed and took a cluster of
grapes from a corner of the basket the peacocks had failed to invade.

"You won't drive them away with a word as
mild as that," he told her. "They own this
place, you know."

He offered her some of the fruit. When she
refused, he plucked a handful of the golden
globes for himself and ate them singly and
without haste while he watched her remon-
strating with the insolent fowl.

All at once she turned back to him with an
astonished stare. "Look!" She held up an elegant white feather the strutting bird had shed
at her feet. But when she saw the knowing
glance Marcello returned, she let it drift down
onto the tabletop, saying in a disinterested
tone, "I'll leave it here for one of the villagers
to find."

"Do what you want with it," he said, but he
brought his rangy body up from the bench
with a languid stretch and reached out for the
talisman the taxi driver had told Gina to
watch out for.

"You could even wear it," he suggested.
Setting his head to one side, he advanced
toward her with the feather in his hand. "You
could wear it next to your heart, like a real
Portuguese *senhorita.*"

Gina discovered that her mouth had gone

dry and that her heart's rhythm was lost in an uneven pounding.

"Wouldn't I look grand, strolling through the streets of Alfama with a plume sprouting from by bosom!"

He stopped in front of her, his eyes the color of the sky. "I rather think you would," he said, and took her in his arms and kissed her.

# Chapter Four

Gina was unshakeable in her refusal to accompany Isabel and Claudio to dinner and then on to the Casa de Fado where at midnight Isabel began her songs.

"Please excuse me tonight," Gina begged before Claudio arrived. "I still have a little leftover jet lag."

When Marcello had said goodbye on the street half-an-hour before, she had discovered she was so weary she could hardly climb the stairs.

More than that, she needed time alone to put Marcello's kiss into perspective. She was accustomed to Quentin Bromley's businesslike pecks or—when he was in a rare erotic mood—to bone-crushing embraces that made her wonder if he even realized he was holding another human being.

But Marcello had enfolded her with a gentleness that was more powerful than Quentin's firmest grip. He had taken her lips as if they belonged to him, and kissed her so deeply and so satisfyingly that the memory of his mouth had pulsed on hers, all the way down from the Castle of St. George, and through the winding streets of Alfama where caged canaries sang in the tenement windows. The air was redolent with springtime smells though it was past the middle of September.

Bemused, she touched her hair and said to Isabel, "I'm a mess. I'm grimy from head to toe."

Isabel reminded, "There is running water. And we are not going out until ten."

"I'll be sound asleep by then." Gina looked longingly past Isabel to the glistening white tub. "I'll go with you tomorrow night. I promise."

But suddenly she became aware of Isabel's aloof demeanor, made all the more impressive by the scarlet pajamas she wore and the way she stood patting her foot in the doorway.

She was angry, Gina realized with a sinking sensation. And why shouldn't she be? Her cousin had spent the day in the company of the man with whom she was in love!

"Isabel . . ." Gina's voice took on a note of pleading. "Could you sit down a minute? I have something to say."

"If it's about Marcello, I am not listening."

"Oh, dear, you are angry, aren't you?"

"My sweet cousin from America." Isabel drew herself up to her full height. "Today I was so furious—like the bull with the *banderillas* stuck into him." She tossed her black mane. "I am the *fadista!* I am not a woman men come to asking for someone else."

"Isabel, I'm so sorry!"

"I told Claudio when he arrived after Marcello to go away!" She pointed dramatically toward the door. "'Do not come back until I control my temper,'" I said.

She let her drooping eyelids down. "But later I called him," she said in a milder tone, "and he *returned* to cheer me up. My darling Claudio is very good at this."

Gina sat hunched in her chair. For Marcello, a man she cared nothing about, she had offended her cousin who was doing everything she could to make her stay in Lisbon pleasant. "This is dreadful," Gina moaned.

"Wait a minute, please. Allow me to speak." Isabel sat down with dignity in a high-backed chair. "This morning I was angry. I paced up and down. I was so angry that I threw a pot from the window into the street, and while I was watching, it was run over by a taxi."

Gina stared. Suddenly Isabel's face wreathed itself in smiles. "When I saw that pot smashed," she said with sparkling eyes, "I realized all at once what a silly woman I was. You are my dear cousin, whom I have waited

54

twenty-four years to see, and I was acting as though you were Mrs. King."

"Who could blame you?" said Gina, stunned. "I know how you feel toward Marcello and I still went out with him. . . ."

"And why not, my darling Gina?" Isabel leaped up and threw her arms around her. "That is what I am telling you. That is what I am seeing at last. You and Marcello, you are the very best thing! Mrs. King is—how do you say it?—left out in the cold, and you . . ." She closed her eyes and laid her cheek against Gina's. "You are inside by the fire with Marcello, warmed by his kisses, held in his arms. . . ."

"Isabel . . ."

Isabel's eyes popped open. Drawing back, she said earnestly, "I like that picture! Because you see how it is—Marcello doesn't love me whether you are here or whether you are in America."

She placed her hand on the high curve of her breast. "This is the truth that breaks my heart. He cared for Mrs. King, but only before you came! Now he doesn't even know she exists. He cares for you!"

"No, he doesn't!" said Gina hastily. "You're making too much of this. We only went on a picnic together."

Isabel's smile was smug. "I know who came to my door, breaking it down before the day was even breaking—looking for you! I know that Claudio told me that you are attracted to

Marcello. I owe it to Claudio for this generous understanding I have reached."

Gina sighed. This had been a most unsettling day. Four hours sleep had not prepared her for it. She tried again, patiently, to talk sense to Isabel.

"You see, I've known men like Marcello . . ." But that wasn't true, she realized unwillingly. Marcello was different in some special way she was afraid to think about. He was romantic, she was sure he was untrustworthy—but still he was different somehow.

She plunged ahead in her explanation to Isabel, determined to disregard that discovery. "A man like Marcello is intrigued by any woman he meets for the first time, but especially a foreign woman, and particularly one who is planning to marry another man."

Isabel frowned. "Claudio says you are not planning to marry."

Blast Claudio! thought Gina. He was, as Marcello had said, a matchmaker—and worse, he was a gossip! "My engagement is not definitely settled but . . ." Where did she stand with Quentin? No matter how tired she was, tonight she must write him a letter. Before she slept, she must clear her head of nonsense.

She tried again to clarify her position. "At some later date I'm sure I will marry Quentin. It's just that last night it annoyed me that Mrs. King made a premature announcement of something that was none of her business."

Isabel nodded solemnly. "It was also annoying for Claudio to pry at breakfast."

Gina wondered numbly if there were anything Claudio had not told Isabel. She groped for her train of thought. "So Claudio . . . No! I mean Marcello! Marcello asked me to go with him on a picnic."

Isabel leaned forward, her eyes bright. "Where was this picnic?"

"At the Castle of St. George. With peacocks and pheasants in attendance."

"How exciting!" Isabel clapped her hands. "Only geese chase me when I go there."

"Next time, take cheese," Gina suggested with utmost sincerity. Isabel stared at her in surprise, and then they both collapsed in hysterical laughter.

"Oh, Isabel . . ." Gina wrapped her arms around her cousin's shoulders when they were calm again. "I'm sorry you had such a rotten day because of me. I could have at least come by and spoken to you before I went off with Marcello."

Isabel shook her head vigorously. "That is not something I should have advised you to do. If you had come before Claudio had helped me to reach this excellent understanding of myself, I might have thrown you out of the window instead of my cooking pot."

She smiled engagingly. "Now I feel so happy I think I cannot sing well tonight. Maybe I will stay home with you and make a nice *caldeirada*, a nice fish stew. We will eat it with bread and red wine and tell each other's fortunes."

Gina went limp again. "For tonight, can we skip the stew and fortunes?" she pleaded. "All I can think of is heading straight to bed."

Isabel's eyes widened. "No! You must not do that!"

Gina halted on her way to the bedroom, ready to weep from weariness. "Please don't insist that I go out with you and Claudio!"

"I am not! But I do insist you cannot lie down on my satin sheets with all that grime you claim came from the Castle of St. George! That I will not allow—even if you are my dearest cousin from America."

Regally, she swept past Gina. "For you, I will draw a nice hot bath!"


The next few days were a blend of pleasure and torment for Gina. The harder she tried to dismiss Marcello Severa from her mind, the more firmly he seemed implanted there. She heard nothing from him, and she told herself she was grateful, but still she listened constantly for the ringing of the telephone.

She went once to the Casa de Fado, but he did not appear, and on succeeding nights, Isabel made no mention of him. Gina had no idea whether he was with Sylvia or if he had simply disappeared from the face of the earth.

Her happiest times were when she was away from the apartment and its silent telephone, touring on her own around Lisbon. In its bustling streets, she was able to forget for a while that a man she had known so casually and so briefly had exercised a profound enough effect on her to make her edgy and discontented.

Once on a buying trip, Gina had spent a week in London, and she was fascinated to see the ways in which the Portuguese expressed their admiration for the British in their workaday world. Green double-decker buses, much like those found in England, plowed up and down the streets. High tea was served in hotel lounges, and in quaint little pubs that could have been lifted out of Picadilly, Portuguese men sipped Scotch whiskey.

But in other ways, she found Lisbon unique. She was intrigued by the layers of row houses that paved its seven hills and by the beautiful tiles called *azulejos* that faced many of the structures along the avenues. Mosaics of rough-cut black-and-white stones made the sidewalks spectacular, and in one district she saw windmills, and in tiny courtyards even goats and sheep grazed. After lunch when the shops were closed during the brief siesta time, Gina rested, too, wherever she found a bench that afforded an interesting view.

One afternoon she took a cab and visited the Ethnological Museum and the Jeronimos Monastery. Another time she wandered through the Baixa and Chiado shopping districts, studying the jewelry and fashions with her own shop in mind.

By the end of the week, however, she had exhausted the sightseeing spots available to her. She was contemplating spending the weekend on the farm with Emilio and Valentina when Isabel casually announced, as they were dressing on Friday night to go out to dinner, that the next evening they were going to a party in Estoril.

Gina remembered that this was the resort town where Claudio leased his villa, and she assumed that it was he who would be their host.

"What kind of party is Claudio having?" she asked Isabel, who cut her black eyes away and murmured, "It is not Claudio who has invited us. It is Mrs. King."

"Sylvia King?" Gina's brush halted in mid-air. Marcello would be there, of course. She said quickly, "I doubt if I can attend. I'm thinking of going to the farm tomorrow."

A string of unfamiliar Portuguese words spewed out of Isabel as she drew on a black stocking. In English she said, "How are you getting to the farm? Is Marcello taking you?"

"Of course not."

Prancing into the bathroom Isabel called back over the sound of running water, "Then you cannot go because I am not letting you run away to Alentejo in my car when I need you here to hold my hand at Sylvia King's house."

Gina smiled in spite of the distress caused by the sound of Marcello's name. "Claudio can hold your hand. I'll take a bus to_the farm."

"Good . . . if you don't want to arrive until next year!" Isabel sailed out of the bathroom shaking a finger in Gina's direction. "If you need fresh air, stick your head out of the window. For loneliness, call Bromley in Nantucket. But do not go off and leave me when I feel so nervous about going to this party where I'm being asked to sing for the first time in a private house."

"Oh, Isabel, how wonderful!" Gina's enthusiasm was as real as her surprise. Had Sylvia King actually been generous enough to arrange such an opportunity for Isabel? It seemed out of character, though Isabel had spoken in Sylvia's presence of her wish for a wider audience than the small Casa de Fado could accommodate.

According to Isabel, in recent months many who were interested in hearing her had been turned away so frequently from the crowded club that they had stopped coming. In Estoril perhaps Sylvia would have as her guests the elite from that suburb. It was a chance to perform that Isabel could not afford to miss. No wonder she was nervous!

"But what will you do about your club engagement?"

"I will return in time to sing there." Isabel stood before her cousin, her huge eyes pleading. "Say you will stay by my side . . . yes?"

Who could resist such an appeal? thought

Gina, nodding her assent. There had been times when she had longed to shake Claudio for fawning over Isabel, but the impulse was certainly understandable when she looked like that.

Watching as Isabel applied her make-up, Gina even felt a little sorry for Claudio. In a way her beautiful cousin was using him because she was impressed by his title.

But it was also true, Gina reflected, that Claudio was impressed by Isabel's popularity as a *fadista*. He loved to be seen with her when crowds congregated around her. Obviously he was jealous of the place Marcello occupied in Isabel's thoughts, but he was not beyond admiring another woman, even one he professed to dislike. The night Marcello and Sylvia had come to their table, Claudio had scarcely been aware of anything except Sylvia King's bright lips moving like the petals of an animated rose in the creamy setting provided by her flawless skin.

What color were Sylvia's eyes? Gina wondered, picking up her brush again. Were they blue like Marcello's? But she could recall only the icy, expressionless stare the heiress had turned on Marcello and herself as they danced.

Would he dance with her again at the party?

The day they had spent together at the Castle of St. George seemed like a dream now. She was convinced that Marcello had not thought about it since they had said goodbye in the street. An enviable attitude, she told herself, pulling grimly at a tangle. It was an attitude she would do well to imitate.

And then she remembered with a pang that she was behaving in a similar fashion toward Quentin. The night of the picnic she had fallen asleep before she thought of the letter she had meant to write. Since then she had scarcely thought of him at all. He deserved to hear from her at once. Besides, she wasn't looking forward to another night at the Casa de Fado in Claudio's company.

"Isabel . . ." She turned around from the mirror. "Do you mind if I don't go along tonight?"

"But you are dressed!" Isabel appeared scandalized by what she obviously considered an outrageous suggestion. Furthermore, she reminded, Gina had stayed at home for the past three nights.

"What will you do here?" she demanded. "Will you sit on my sofa and make faces at my wallpaper?"

Gina laughed. "I've been putting off writing a letter."

"You are tired of Claudio and me," Isabel accused.

"Of you, never," Gina sidestepped gently. "But I must write to Quentin. I've been neglecting him."

"Ah, yes, *senhor* Quentin Bromley." This was an excuse Isabel could understand. "You are thinking of this American who is begging you to marry him. This is why you want to go to the farm—because there is so much excitement here in Lisbon that you have forgotten about your Quentin. You think of darling Marcello and upset yourself."

Gina flushed, but she made her tone light. "Thinking of him does upset me. I'm embarrassed that all your grand plans for us have come to nothing. He hasn't even called me."

Isabel's look turned stern. "This Marcello is—you know how to say it—a chump! He is wasting a whole week to make you feel jealous!"

Gina laughed self-consciously. "What makes you think he's doing that?"

"Because he comes to the Casa de Fado with Mrs. King."

"Oh . . ." Gina was suddenly busy, opening drawers, closing them. "Have you finished with the mascara?"

"When Claudio and I arrive there together and you are not with us, I can see that Marcello is displeased. He does not come to our table. He broods and does not make jokes."

"He is absorbed in Mrs. King."

"He is making you think this is true." Isabel's sniff said plainly what she thought of such a scheme. "But I am making sure you know it means nothing."

Gina made no answer. Sitting down on the couch, she unstrapped her sandals. Wild horses couldn't drag her to the Casa de Fado now. She would have to decide later what to do about tomorrow.

* * *

The apartment grew uncomfortably quiet after Isabel and Claudio left, and for a time Gina wandered restlessly from room to room, not allowing herself to dwell on what Isabel had said about Marcello, but feeling the effects of it just the same.

His kiss had stirred up desires she was happier not thinking about, and yet these feelings had continued throughout the week to nag her. It irritated her that the touch of a man's lips—any man's lips, but especially Marcello's—could exert that much control over her emotions.

But as she had observed before, Marcello was not just any man. He was uncommonly attractive, with elusive qualities she hadn't been able to pinpoint, and he was wiser in his ways of dealing with women than he had any right to be.

She had expected to freeze him out, and instead he had turned a cold shoulder to her. If he had called her again the day after the picnic, or the day after that, she would have been assured that he was behaving according to pattern, a virile male pursuing a promising beginning. But obviously he wasn't that eager for pursuit, and his neglect piqued her interest as little else could have.

Had he found her kiss as cold as her attitude toward her father? Was that why she hadn't heard from him? Or had he found her response too eager? A sinking sensation seized her each time she wondered how much she had revealed of the chaos that had surged through her when his warm, challenging mouth had turned moistly on hers.

Angered that after all this time she was still subjecting herself to pointless cross-examination, Gina concentrated on undressing, on folding her lacy underclothes back into a drawer and hanging up the ruffled blouse and casually tailored wool skirt she would have worn to the Casa de Fado.

But when everything was neatly put away, she lingered naked in front of the mirror, trying to see with the eyes of a man her lean, supple body, the neat curves of her diaphragm where it tucked in at her waist, and her high, rounded breasts. But nothing she saw set her apart from a million other women who were careful of their diets and got the proper exercise.

Where was the secret ingredient lodged that drew one man and one woman together, that made each of them certain that no one else held the key to their happiness?

Probably such a thing existed only in melodrama.

Sighing, she told herself that she was so absurdly sensitive to Marcello's treatment of her because she was depressed, and depression—in her experience, at least—had its roots in indecision. She remembered that before she made up her mind about the shop, she had been like a caged tiger. Not having a direct course to follow was like being mired in mud. One strained forward and pulled back-

ward to the point of exhaustion and got no-
where.

Absentmindedly, she ran a hand over her
flat stomach and then she lifted her hair from
her neck. What she needed most was to make
up her mind about Quentin.

It had been a mistake to run away to Portugal, she decided, taking out of the closet an
expensive dressing gown of whispering silk,
cream-colored and bound in black braid. Gina
had never indulged in luxury items, but a
flaw in the hem of this robe had prevented her
from offering it for sale in her shop, and once
she had discovered the erotic pleasure the
slithering silk gave to her nakedness, she
wondered how she had existed so long without
it. She often wore it, and nothing else, when
she was alone in the evenings. Wrapping herself in it now, she luxuriated in the caress of
the cloth and headed toward the kitchen.

She heated a cup of soup and drank it,
standing by the sink, staring out into the
darkness. Grapes filled a bowl on the cabinet,
and she ate a handful, remembering that
most of her attention had been fixed on Marcello sensuously devouring this same kind of
fruit when the white peacock had dropped at
her feet the talisman of marriage.

Hastily she went into the living room and
took a sheet of white notepaper from the desk
drawer. Dear Quentin . . .

Dear predictable Quentin. No pulses leaped
at his name sounding in her brain. She
chewed the tip of her pen, her brow furrowed

until she could call up his sturdy likeness . . .
his square jaw, his thin-lipped smile . . .

Quentin is dear in many respects, she told
herself sternly. It was he who had provided
her firmest support when she was trying to
make up her mind about carrying on with the
shop. His legal advice had been invaluable,
and until the business got on its feet, his
unwavering optimism had been the only thing
that had brought her over the rough spots.

Of course he had never hidden the fact that
his chief preoccupation, at first, was watching
her resurrect a dying business. That she was
an attractive woman was not nearly so important as the proof that she was a capable
woman who was success-oriented. Only after
the shop was turning a handsome profit had
he observed with detached interest that its
owner wore her clothes with more flair than
her customers did and that she could talk as
sensibly as any man on any number of sub-
jects.

Quentin definitely had his blind spots, and
Gina had never tried to fool herself on that
score, but at the same time she refused to
believe that there was anything regrettable in
Quentin's attitude. Why shouldn't admiration
and respect be as sound a basis for marriage
as any other? What difference did it make that
he would rather discuss politics or a recent
Supreme Court ruling than to hold her in his
arms?

No difference. None whatsoever. Dear

Quentin, she began again. Since I've been away, I have thought a great deal about your wanting to marry me, and I think that very soon I'll be able to give you an answer.

Actually, that penchant Quentin had for ignoring her physically was a relief in many ways. He was not a romantic, and that was his greatest attraction. The romance of her father's escapades and the "charming" way he had of forgetting about people who cared for him until he needed them to help him out of a scrape had tainted her life.

But still . . .

She laid down her pen with an ache, recalling the brilliant smile and craggy, creased face of Christian Thomas. A rush of memories flooded her mind. She pictured his virile, youthful form bent over the rigging of his boat the last time she saw him alive. She had passed on by without stopping—a stubbornness she knew she would regret to the end of her days—but she had heard his resonant, low-pitched voice coming after her, calling softly: Beautiful legs . . . She had imagined the crooked smile he gave to the deckhand who was letting out the rope. My beautiful daughter has beautiful legs. . . .

What did he care if she had a beautiful mind! Or a courageous spirit! With one breath he could make her feel precious and special, and with the next, cheap and common. He had been romantic enough for ten men, and she and her mother had paid the price so often for his infidelities that she was sick to death of all charming men, all handsome men . . . all men like Marcello Severa.

They were poison, she thought coldly, and concentrated again on Quentin's virtues. Though he had a rough-hewn appealing look, what one noticed most was his brusque, no-nonsense approach to life. One looked at Quentin Bromley and thought of respectability, of steadfastness and unflinching principles. A woman married to him would be the only woman in his life. Her only rival would be the law.

Suddenly Gina's breath caught in her throat. Snatching up the sheet of white paper, she crumpled it in her fist.

She was stupid, she thought furiously, to envy, even momentarily, a woman like Sylvia King because a man like Marcello Severa took her to bed—as quite obviously he did.

It was silly to envy the way Claudio looked at Isabel when she, Gina, would not have Claudio if he were the last man on earth!

Why couldn't she be thankful that everything in her own life was proceeding exactly as it should? When this trip was over, Quentin would be waiting in Nantucket, offering the solid family structure she had coveted all her life. With Quentin there would be no surprises, no upsets like the one Marcello had given her with a single kiss. When she was married to Quentin, life would stretch before her as placidly as a summer sea. . . .

Her hand gripped tighter the crumpled start

of her letter. Her throat tightened, and she imagined a door inside her closing . . . a key turning in a lock.

If she became Mrs. Quentin Bromley, that door would never be opened. No one would ever look into her heart. No one would ever really know her. Silk against her skin would always have to be the substitute for the passionate touch of a man who feverishly adored her. She would grow old and remain as the world saw her now: self-made, independent, resilient . . .

And terribly, terribly lonely.

A clammy sweat broke out on her temples, and beneath her dressing gown she sensed her flesh withering. Inside her there was— there had always been—a woman clamoring to be let out, a woman who was Christian Thomas's daughter, and Marcello Severa's kiss had made it all but impossible to restrain her.

# Chapter Five

Claudio came over from Estoril early in the afternoon of Sylvia's party, sat in the living room drinking port, and smoked cigarettes while he offered words that were purported to be encouraging to the nervous Isabel.

"Sylvia has invited half-a-dozen friends of hers from the watering spots of Europe—men who own clubs in the finest hotels," he called out when Isabel paled and fled to the bedroom.

"Jacques Petrot is one. You've heard me speak of him. And Victor Lagonioli from my own country is another."

He went on and on, ignoring Isabel's moans, and Gina, sitting across from him with a lemonade, wondered how he could be so callous. And how did he know so much about Sylvia's plans? The deep cleft in his chin irritated her unreasonably, and she thought he had no right to be so slickly handsome and so utterly brainless.

Finally she told them she was going for a walk, and went down into the street, but her wanderings were aimless and in half-an-hour she had admitted to herself that she was as nervous about the party as Isabel.

To her relief, she discovered that Isabel had driven Claudio away with the threat that if he didn't vanish immediately she would ring up Sylvia and tell her to find another *fadista* to entertain her friends.

Claudio was horrified, Isabel confided in a more cheerful tone than she had voiced all day, and Gina herself began to feel better.

They talked of other things until it was time to dress, and then Gina began to think again of the unnerving dialogue she had conducted with herself the evening before.

In a way it would be a relief to confront Marcello again, she told herself as she pulled on a long black taffeta skirt. When she saw him with Sylvia, she would be cured of any incipient yearnings that might still pester her.

If she remembered his lips on hers, she could imagine him kissing Sylvia. If he touched her, she could think of the many times his arms had held the American beauty he had spent the whole week with!

She assured herself that there were bound to be other attractive men at the party. If the side of her that belonged more to the nature of

Christian Thomas than to her dead mother demanded center stage, she could concentrate her attentions on someone less threatening than Marcello . . . though she hated herself for fearing the power he held over her.

In her anguish last night, she had not been able to write the letter to Quentin after all, and when she had crawled into bed and finally fallen asleep, Marcello had been the object of her dreams. It was she, not his nursemaid, he was hiding from in the ruins of the castle, and when he at last emerged dressed like the guard the nursemaid had covertly kissed, Marcello had kissed Gina lingeringly, passionately, until she awakened trembling and aroused and yearning for reality in place of illusion.

Fighting that memory she pulled on a sparkling black beaded top, held up by spaghetti straps and fitted as neatly as skin to the curves of her breast. She wore a wide scarlet cummerbund and a pale silk rose, fastened to the side sweep of her hair, which completed her outfit. She left her throat bare, and small gold earrings were her only jewelry.

When Isabel saw her, she exclaimed, "My goodness! You are enchanting, my darling."

Isabel herself looked ravishing. For this occasion she had abandoned the traditionally dark colors of the *fadista,* retaining only her fringed shawl to set off the layered white ruffles of *crepe de chine* that rippled around her formfitting gown.

74

"When I move," she complained, "I am able to take only tiny steps, like this mermaid we have all heard of who balances on the forks of her tail!"

But she was enormously pleased with her appearance and when Claudio arrived and commented that she was a knockout, she shed her nervousness and trailed down the stairs to his car with regal poise.

Gina followed, wishing she weren't always the third party, but unable to fault Claudio, who was doing everything in his power to keep her from feeling superfluous.

He was almost too agreeable, she decided from the back seat, when they had begun the half-hour drive to Estoril. Gazing out of the window, she admired the bathing beaches that followed the coast, the lanky palms, and brilliant roses spilling over walls on every side, but her thoughts kept straying to the controlled excitement she had sensed in Claudio's bright, ferretlike eyes. She wondered if he were tense because of Isabel's upcoming performance, or if grand parties always affected him this way. To her, he seemed on a high, but not one that was drug induced. Finally she concluded that it really made no difference what had turned him on, and she dismissed him from her thoughts.

She had her own butterflies to contend with! In a few minutes she would be seeing Marcello again . . . and hearing his voice. . . . She ran the tip of her tongue over her dry lips and longed for a sip of water. Nervously, she picked at a loose thread on her cummerbund, but nothing relaxed her until Sylvia's villa rose in front of the windshield. Then she forgot everything in her admiration of the elegant spectacle it presented perched before them at the edge of the sea.

Though it was a fall evening, the air was balmy. The setting sun had left a lean row of purple clouds on the horizon, and in front of them stood Sylvia's mansion, spread out on several levels, gleaming white, its garden aglow with hundreds of tiny, twinkling lights. Waves lapped at the narrow shore and as soon as they had alighted from the car, they could hear the delicate tinkling sounds of an orchestra playing on the terrace nearest the water.

Isabel grew nervous again and clung to Claudio's arm, but Gina felt a miraculous calm spreading through her. This was all too unreal. The villa was like a cloud castle and the guests would be fantasies, too, not real people. She had nothing to fear from Marcello or from Sylvia. This was not Gina Thomas's world. She had floated in from another planet and could as easily float out again, free of every encumbrance that had haunted her since her arrival in Lisbon.

Following Isabel and Claudio, she moved up the stairs in a state of euphoria, drinking in the costly extravagance of marbled hallways, exquisite paintings, fabulous statuary. Crowds of elegantly dressed men and women drifted through the rooms with glasses of champagne in their hands and smiles painted on their aristocratic faces.

But nothing about Gina's bearing betrayed that such opulence was new to her. Claudio, studying her over the rim of his glass, felt mildly depressed that she showed in no way that her surroundings impressed her, and Isabel gazed with open envy on her poised assurance.

Until the guests were ushered into a number of parlors and drawing rooms where tables had been set up for dinner, Gina was surrounded by an animated and constantly changing group of Sylvia's friends. She wondered where Marcello was, but she caught no glimpse of him until she found herself being seated in the main dining room and she spotted him and Sylvia sitting down at the head of the table.

Sylvia wore an emerald-colored dress of an airy cloth that skimmed her body and yet managed to show off to peak advantage her petite form. As before, her blonde hair was drawn back into a low chignon that hung just above her nape. Diamonds glittered at her throat and from her earlobes, and she exuded an air of saccharine charm.

At her side Marcello's copper-colored skin gleamed in striking contrast to the silver streaks in his hair and to the black jacket that molded his wide shoulders.

Gina was watching when his gaze skipped

down the table, met hers, and locked with it. At once the room and everything in it receded. Marcello seemed to sit alone at the other end of the table. Between them there hung in the perfumed air a charged field and a current of excitement was generated that flowed continuously.

The image persisted even after Gina pulled her glance away and the meal began. Enthralled, she was scarcely conscious of what she ate or what she said to either of her dinner partners. She did not look at Marcello again, but she felt his eyes upon her, and before the dessert finally came, it seemed she had sat for a hundred years in the candleglow, nodding and smiling, yet dying inside.

Nothing had been solved by her coming here. If anything, she was more drawn to Marcello's rugged good looks than she had been before. Evening clothes made him seem more inaccessible than the faded jeans and checkered shirt he had worn to the castle. He appeared godlike now. Everything about him was magnified all out of proportion . . . even her memories of the way he had held her . . . the way his mouth had come down on hers.

Desperate to regain some sort of equilibrium, she hastily excused herself when the meal was finished and was searching the hallway for some place of retreat when she heard his commanding voice behind her.

"Don't run away, Gina."

Fighting back an urge to do that very thing,

she forced herself to turn around and face him calmly. "I was looking for a powder room."

"There is nothing so simple as that here." Amusement twitched at his lips. "There are lounges with sunken bathtubs and couches and steam closets and probably slaves with palmetto fans." He grinned. "Women have been known to disappear inside them and not come out for days."

If only I could do that! Gina thought, but she maintained her air of calm. "There's no place to duck into quickly and put on fresh lipstick?"

"I'll be your mirror." He took her arm. "But why bother? You look exquisite just the way you are."

With no regard for her hesitation he moved her down the hallway and out through a pair of French doors into a garden. High walls surrounded it. There was a fountain in the middle and only one bench.

"We ought to be able to hide here for a few minutes." He pulled her down beside him and she felt the warmth of his knee pressing against hers. "What have you been doing for the past week?"

As if he cared!

"I've been seeing Lisbon." Over the thundering of her heart she kept her voice steady. He didn't have to know that every step of the way she had wished for him at her side. "It's a wonderful city."

"What do you think of Estoril?"

"This is the only place I've seen." She made herself look away from him to the flowering vines that covered the walls. "I was too caught up to notice anything else."

"This mansion is the showplace of the coast." He gazed serenely at her, his eyes moving first to her lips, then over the glistening beaded front of her blouse. "But it isn't authentic. It was built to impress someone like Sylvia who in turn uses it to impress everyone else who wishes he or she could afford to take up her lease. Did you notice all those hungry looks out there?"

Gina warmed to the laughter in his voice. She felt herself relaxing, coming under his spell. She should fight it. . . . She moistened her lips. "What have you been doing?"

He looked straight at her. "Thinking of you."

A pulse leaped in her throat. "Those are easy words."

"They weren't earned easily. I've gone to the telephone a hundred times since we came down from the castle. Each time I barely stopped short of calling you."

She brought her hands together tightly in her lap. "Why didn't you?"

"Because I don't like to be haunted by a kiss. I don't like a woman I've known for only a few hours to cling so persistently in my thoughts. I wanted to prove to myself that I could resist you."

Her gaze fastened sightlessly on two bright stars and a wisp of moon.

"But I can't resist you," he said. "Come to Sintra tomorrow and spend the day with me."

"How will I get there?" She heard herself speaking, but she couldn't believe what she was saying. No recriminations? No arguments? Where was her pride?

"There's a train," he said. "You take it at a station Isabel can show you. The countryside is beautiful, ever changing. You'll be there before you know it. I'll be waiting."

It was settled as easily as that. An accomplished fact. She was going to spend the day with him. She hadn't written to Quentin and now she could not even remember what he looked like. Her head was too full of the dazzle of Marcello.

A tinkle of laughter sounded beyond them, and then Sylvia was there, radiant with the success of her party, reaching for Marcello's arm, seemingly unperturbed that she had found them together.

"Your cousin is preparing to sing," she told Gina. "My guests are gathering on the rear terrace. Isabel will stand with the water behind her. Don't you think that will be effective, darling?" She turned her face up to Marcello's. "The water is gorgeous tonight. So mysterious, so black with little streaks of silver from the moon. Like your hair, my love." She ran her fingers over it lightly, her touch proprietary.

*He belongs to her*, Gina thought, watching. *But he wants to be with me.*

They went through the house, Sylvia chattering, Marcello attentive, as if he had forgotten that Gina was still at his side. Before Isabel began her first song, Gina had agreed to go sailing with one of the men she had met before dinner and also to have lunch on Monday with the Rumanian duke who had sat on her left at the table.

# Chapter Six

*Sintra* . . . Gina would never forget her first impression of it. She thought that surely it must be the greenest spot on earth.

The little train she caught at Isabel's slightly envious direction chugged inland for seven miles past Estoril and then all at once, rising before her, were verdant hillsides that quickly turned into mountains that were greener still. Velvety moss furred the rocks over which crystal water leaped. Every house was enclosed by a wall and every wall was coated with green lichen, and vine-bound and blossoming.

Castles capped two green, jagged peaks that hovered over the town's stucco dwellings whose colors—red and blue, pink, orange and yellow—dotted the landscape like flowers.

Everywhere an air of timelessness prevailed. Sintra seemed a place the clock had forgotten, and when Gina stepped down from the train and saw Marcello standing on the platform, the strange sensation came over her that he had been waiting for her forever. She came easily into his arms and took his light kiss of welcome as naturally as if she experienced it daily.

It was only when they were in his car and moving swiftly through the countryside toward his villa that a sense of reality caught up with her. What was she doing here? What did she expect of this day?

Her glance went quickly toward Marcello. He smiled back lazily. With one hand resting casually on the steering wheel, he reached with his other hand for hers and pulled it into his lap, the blunt end of his thumb sensuously massaging her fingertips.

"Such capable little hands," he murmured thoughtfully. "The hands of a businesswoman."

Gina tensed. It was the first comment he had made since they got into the car, and she wasn't sure that it was a compliment. Was that another reason he wanted to resist her, because she worked for a livelihood? The women he knew all had money. Lots of it.

He had asked no questions about her train ride either. It was as if he meant to lock out of their day all reminders of an outside world.

Gina panicked. Taking her hand back into

her own lap, she said, "What did you think of Isabel's songs last night?"

His glance flicked over her, but he answered without hesitation, "She was the hit of the evening."

Gina warmed to the sincerity of that simple statement. She had been so proud of Isabel! So thrilled to see that the moment her cousin stepped upon the raised dais provided for her, all uncertainty had left her. She sang with the same haunting conviction with which she charmed her audiences in Alfama. Her luminous eyes had sent out a sad searching over the hushed crowd and Gina had been awed by the picture she created and with Sylvia's choice of setting.

Isabel's white dress had stood out against the backdrop of the black sea with startling contrast. The moon made a halo seemingly appear behind her hair, and she had sung with such heartbreaking beauty that for minutes after the sound of her voice ceased, no one breathed. Then thunderous applause had resounded across the marble terrace.

Gina sighed with pleasure, remembering it. "I thought it was a stunning performance. I hadn't realized Isabel was quite so professional."

"I think she has grown into the finest singer of fado in Portugal," said Marcello. "Did you go back with her and Claudio to the Casa de Fado?"

Gina nodded. "There were even some of Sylvia's guests who followed her there to hear her sing again. The place was packed. It was a good evening."

Marcello commented wryly, "I suppose Claudio was beside himself."

Oddly, Gina felt called upon to defend Isabel's Italian count. "Naturally, he was proud of Isabel. He was nervous for her, I think. He could hardly contain himself on the way to Estoril."

"Of course," said Marcello darkly. "That sleek devil thrives on complications."

"What do you mean?"

Marcello cleared his black look with a smile. "Never mind. Is there too much wind?"

"No, I'm fine." Still puzzling over Marcello's strange remark, Gina asked, "Were the entrepreneurs Sylvia invited to hear Isabel sing pleased with her performance?"

Marcello's look darkened again. "How did you know about them?"

"Claudio told us they would be there. They were friends of his."

"Actually, they were friends of mine. I specifically asked Sylvia not to mention their presence."

"Whose party was it?" Gina snapped. "Yours or Sylvia's?"

"I suppose you could say it was mine," Marcello answered easily. "It was my idea. I wanted a broader stage for Isabel because I think fado should be appreciated all across

Europe. I asked Sylvia to be the hostess since she dotes on social affairs, and I'm not particularly fond of them."

Gina was too surprised to speak for a minute. Isabel would be thrilled out of her mind that Marcello had gone to such trouble for her!

"You're very kind," she finally stammered.

"Perhaps not. It's too bad Isabel found out she was auditioning. Nothing may come of it, and then she'll be disappointed."

"Are you saying that you think your friends might not have liked what they heard?"

"Not at all. They were genuinely impressed, but the entertainment business is complicated. Bringing in new talent depends upon a variety of factors. It could be months before anything definite is decided. Isabel could have been spared the torture of waiting if Claudio had kept quiet."

Gina answered crisply, "Don't forget . . . the information didn't originate with Claudio."

Marcello glanced across at her. "You don't care much for Sylvia, do you?"

"We haven't much in common."

"Oh, I don't know. You're both American . . . and you're both beautiful."

Gina accepted the compliment without betraying how much it pleased her. "That's as far as you can go, isn't it, in your search for similarities?"

"You both know Quentin Bromley."

Gina ignored the barb. "You spoke of the entertainment business as if you had first-hand knowledge of it."

"Only from an observer's standpoint." But he saw his answer hadn't satisfied her and he went on in a casual tone. "I thought for a time it might be interesting to own a nightclub. I spent six months touring the major capitals and researching the matter."

This new aspect of Marcello fascinated Gina. "What was your conclusion?"

"That it would bore me silly inside of a year. But I met some interesting people. The men who were at the party were among them."

Gina was silent for a few miles, considering his comments and missing the robust scenery flashing past. Then suddenly Marcello turned up a winding drive and her attention was captured by the charming old house that appeared before them, set behind a garden that was luminous in color.

The houses she had seen as they passed through Sintra were made of stucco, but this one was constructed from stone, gray and weathered, and mossy in shadowed corners. A salmon-colored bougainvillaea had climbed up one side to the second story, and its vibrant blossoms framed windows where filmy curtains were pulled back to reveal rows of flowering geraniums in pots along the sills. A low stone fence surrounded the garden, and in front of the carved front door a white cat slept with her tail curled around to her nose.

Marcello saw that Gina was speechless.

When he had stopped the car at the gate, he turned to her and said with a pleased look, "It isn't what you expected, is it?"

"Not in the least. But I love it!"

"It was my grandfather's house. When I was a boy, I came here whenever I could. I think in those days I liked it mostly because it was tucked away up here in the hills, and I was accustomed to the plains of Alentejo where there was no place to hide."

Gina's sparkling glance fell on him. "Were you in need of hiding places?"

"Always," he answered with mock solemnity. "Someone was constantly after me to comb my hair or clean my fingernails."

"I can't believe you were a grubby little boy." As usual Marcello was attired in jeans and one of the fine shirts he wore as casually as if he had bought it in a street stall. His skin carried the tantalizing scent of his shaving lotion—a fresh woodsy fragrance Gina sometimes smelled in her dreams.

She herself wore an American perfume, and a dress she had put on for the train ride. But in her overlarge purse she carried her corduroy jeans and a pink oxford cloth shirt with a matching Shetland sweater. The crisp, sunny day seemed made for hiking. Suddenly, joy surged through her like a burst of a bird's song.

"Can we get out?" But she already had her hand on the door handle, and Marcello laughed.

"You want to see if my house is as wholesome inside as it looks from the outside, don't you? Well, I can tell you it is. The same woman cares for it as she did in my grandfather's time. She has help now—granddaughters of her own who are always underfoot—but she is in complete command of it, and of me as well."

Lucia was the housekeeper's name. She was old and bustling. Her frame, draped in the customary black of Portuguese women, was ample and rotund, her shoulders were stooped. But she had the merry laugh of a girl, and bright twinkling eyes that made her drab costume appear only a dark setting for diamonds. Gina loved her at once.

Lucia had prepared lunch for them which one of her granddaughters served on the back terrace under the sheltering limbs of an oak. Beyond the edge of the garden a stream danced and bubbled down from the mountain, and the white cat came around to sit on the wall and stare placidly as they ate.

"Oh, Marcello," Gina lounged back in her chair, lazy and contented when the meal was finished, "why do you bother to keep a place in Lisbon when everything anybody could ever want is here?"

Hands clasped behind his head, he studied the even features of her profile and drawled inscrutably, "Today perhaps everything I want is in Sintra."

Gina's heartbeat quickened, but he made no move to approach her. The table was cleared by the same shy, dark-haired girl who had set it, and still he seemed satisfied to sit on in the dappled sunlight, speaking quietly of various aspects of the countryside and listening with his usual concentration to her corresponding remarks.

He had not touched her since she took her hand away in the car. When he led her through the house on a tour of inspection, he had been affable and pleased at her appreciation of its serene beauty, but he had stayed a comfortable distance from her in both manner and presence.

It was an enchanting but frustrating interlude, and Gina found herself getting edgy as the sun moved to the flowers bordering the terrace. Her train left at five. A little more than three hours remained of her visit. How did Marcello propose to spend them?

Strenuously, she soon discovered. He suggested they have some coffee and then he announced that he was glad she had brought clothes appropriate for hiking.

She replied, only half-teasing, "Did you dig around in my bag while I was out in the kitchen, thanking Lucia for lunch?" The uncanny way he had of sensing small things about her disturbed her. "I've brought jeans and a shirt. You must have seen them."

His eyes showed faint amusement. "I did, but not on my own initiative. That knapsack, or whatever you call that thing you're carrying, opened at the train station when you tipped the porter who helped you off. I think I saw a sweater, too." He angled up out of his chair. "Bring it along. The sun will set behind the mountain soon, and then the air turns chilly.

Gina wore her sweater, but the pace Marcello set for the climb made it unnecessary. Their destination was the Castelo dos Mouros, a ruined Moorish castle built in the eighth century. The path they followed rose almost straight up through the trees.

"It looks . . ." Gina, toasty-warm and enthralled, chewed her lip pensively, "it looks like the quintessence of every castle that was ever built." Her eyes grew starry. "There was one just like it painted on the cover of my book of fairy tales when I was a child. Exactly the same domes and turrets! I know it was this castle."

"You have an excellent memory," Marcello commented. He leaned against a poplar, arms folded, watching her, a ghost of a smile on his lips.

When she turned and saw him looking at her, the thought passed through her mind that like the castle's pose across the valley, this was Marcello's quintessential pose. This was the way he appeared in her dreams: aloof, masterful, and so fascinatingly virile that desire stirred within her like a living thing.

Reluctantly she took her eyes away and fixed her gaze again on the distant palace. "One doesn't forget early impressions," she answered in a voice not quite steady.

"Some impressions of later life are indelible, too." He pushed away from the tree and came toward her, drawing her glance back to watch with mounting excitement his purposeful stride and the same direct look he leveled on her when he took her in his arms the day of their picnic.

But before he reached her, he stopped—so near she feared he might feel the vibrations of her yearning, but distant enough so that she saw, yet could not touch, the texture of his skin, the springing curls of hair where his shirt pulled apart.

She wondered if when she swallowed he could see how tight her throat was. Had he spotted the pulse leaping at her temple? The button fastening his shirt pocket rose . . . fell. She saw his lips part.

"Shall I tell you about the castle?" he said.

Shock waves ripped through her. "Please do," but the words came out flat with disappointment. She sat down, weak-kneed, on a fallen tree trunk, furious at herself. Marcello's move was calculated. She was sure he had meant to evoke exactly that response from her, and the glint in his eyes told her that he saw he had succeeded.

She said, "I'm sure it has a fascinating history."

"A romantic one, at least."

Gina dug her fingernails into the rotting bark. "Castles by their very nature are romantic."

"But the people who live in them aren't

always. They behead one another and lock each other up in dungeons."

He sat down beside her. "This was not the case, however, with the Castelo de Pena. Ferdinand, who was the young king-consort of Queen Maria II, was of Saxe-Coburg descent. He idolized Maria and had the castle built for her. But I think you can see in its similarity to those on the Rhine that he must have been homesick."

The remark caught Gina's imagination and thrilled her, too, that a man of Marcello's temperament could see in stone cupolas and battlemented walls not merely architecture but emotion. For a moment she forgot her pique with him and gazed back across the valley at the palace rising from its skirt of green with such majesty it seemed carved from the mountain itself.

"It's very beautiful."

"It has stood there, looking just that way, since the 1840's." He plucked a stem of grass and folded it between his fingers. "Such permanence appeals to me."

"I share that feeling too," she answered.

That was the moment he kissed her . . . when she was least prepared for the strong pull of his arms turning her toward him and the lowering of his lips as he brought her hard against his chest. As naturally as the castle rose out of the rock mountain, his mouth closed firmly over hers. He held her as he had done before, powerfully, locking her to him and yet enfolding her, caressing her, heating her blood.

With flesh and bones, she acquiesced. Her mind stood apart, no match for her emotions. She revelled in his fingers smoothing her skin, the warm thrust of his hand inside her shirt, molding the curve of her shoulder, her nape, and then—when she was wild with waiting—the sudden opening of the buttons of her blouse and the kissing of the erect mounds of her breasts until shivers of ecstasy made her take his mouth with hers, hotly, fiercely, in joyous abandonment.

Easing her onto the leaf-matted ground, he lay down beside her, one arm beneath her shoulders, the other hand sliding over her body, lingering on the rise of her hip and then returning to her breasts. With gentle kisses, he covered her eyelids. He kissed her lips and the flesh behind her earlobes where the heated oil from her perfume gave forth a dizzying fragrance that mingled with the male scent of his skin.

There was no sense of hurry in Marcello's caresses. Gina was ravenous for his touch, tuned to every muscle tightening in his body as it pressed against her. But he was soon deliberately playful, savoring the kisses he gave her, heightening the tension between them to an unbearable pitch, and at last rocking her over onto his chest, letting her body rise and fall as his lungs worked more slowly, until gradually her own breathing resumed a near normal rhythm. His mouth turned velvet against her lips and then he let her go, bringing her up to a sitting position, plucking from her hair a brown, twisted leaf, brushing from her cheek a bit of silver wing abandoned by a dragonfly.

Blinking, Gina saw that the world around them had turned golden. Shafts of waning sunlight filtered slantwise through the trees. Far up in the sky, birds circled and sang.

Marcello gazed at her, not quite smiling. "Soon it will be dark." He fastened the buttons of her blouse, his fingers setting fire to her skin. "We have to go down."

Gina looked past his shoulder. Her blood was still rushing through her veins, her heart still pumping erratically. But her brain had cleared. They had not made love—but only because Marcello had decided they would not. The part of her that belonged more to Christian Thomas than to her mild-mannered mother had made a fool of herself!

With burning cheeks, she said, "I've missed my train."

"I'll drive you back to Lisbon."

Her shame turned to anger that he could dismiss her so casually. She searched for some clue to what he was thinking in the way he dusted off his jeans and ran his hands through his thick, curling hair . . . in his glance moving over her . . . in his lingering half-smile.

But Marcello kept his own counsel. On the way down the mountain, he moved forward on

his own, ahead of her, holding back obstruct-
ing limbs until she had passed safely by them,
but not reaching out for her hand or laying his
arm across her shoulder. He moved indepen-
dently, in an easy, confident rhythm that required no matching cadence.

# Chapter Seven

For days Gina nursed her anger. Marcello telephoned on Monday, but she was out to lunch with the Rumanian count she had met at Sylvia's party, and though he left a number, she did not return his call.

Then on Wednesday evening when she came in from sailing with the other man who had made a date with her in Estoril, she found the apartment empty. A note from Isabel informed her that she and Claudio had gone shopping and on to his villa for an early dinner before her show.

The apartment windows were open and cries of sleepy babies and the trillings of caged canaries hanging in the doorways along the street came up to her in a melancholy blend of sweetness and sadness. She felt her

anger leaving her, and in its place an emptiness settled in.

The man who had taken her sailing was
older. In some ways—the best ways—he reminded her of her father. He was debonair
and lighthearted and, though he had kissed
her, he had not expected her to take him
seriously. She had been able to relax and
watch the billowing sail and the blue sky fill
with popcornlike clouds.

Eventually his talk came around to Marcello. Obviously he had no idea that Gina was
anything more than a passing acquaintance
of the man he spoke of in such admiring
tones. Marcello, he said, was enormously in-
fluential in Portugal, but because of his
Spanish connections he had kept apart from
politics. But, said the man, he doubted if
Marcello was interested in politics anyway.

What was he interested in? Gina had asked,
veiling her bitterness behind a tight smile.

Her friend had turned thoughtful then, for
the first time all afternoon.

"I think," he said, "that Marcello is an
explorer. Not of continents," he said when he
saw Gina's stare. "Or of space, or of any of
today's frontiers, but of the inner man. The
outward manifestations of the ornery beast
Homo sapien merely amuse him. But the
inner workings, those are what fascinate
him."

The man's eyes narrowed in appreciation.
"He has a keen curiosity about what makes
men tick. And women, too," he added with a

twinkle. "He can never be satisfied until he knows inside and out the person he is dealing with."

He made a joke then and told a story about a scrape the two of them had once gotten into, and then he changed the subject. But Gina had gone on thinking about what he had said.

When she was back at the apartment, she continued to brood. She leaned on her elbows at the windowsill and watched the activity of the street and realized then that her anger was gone.

She had been angry at Marcello because he had brought her straight back to Isabel's apartment and turned her out on the doorstep at eight o'clock on a Sunday evening without even so much as a mention of soup and crackers . . . without a kiss . . . without a word about when they would meet again. She was angry because he had rejected her . . . and most of all because he had awakened in her a self that had behaved like a compliant fool.

But now in the light of what her friend had said, she saw that the whole episode had been no more than an experiment on Marcello's part, an investigation into the nature of one Gina Thomas, female, American. For days she had wasted an enormous amount of emotional energy on an incident that was mere routine to Marcello.

Her feelings of emptiness continued, and she pulled herself away from the window to undress, pondering as she removed her clothes the truth that until now she had not been able to face.

The episode at Sintra had been monumental to her, she acknowledged painfully, because Marcello meant more to her than she had allowed herself to admit. From the start she had known what kind of man he was and how much damage he was capable of doing to anyone stupid enough to become involved with him. She had known since she was fifteen that men like Marcello were heartless. And still she had let herself be fooled by him. She had convinced herself that he was different . . . that she mattered to him in some special way. It was important to her to believe that because Marcello mattered to her.

Wrapping her silk robe in comforting folds around her body, she sat down on the side of the bed, fighting a quickening sense of loss. She had come to Portugal shrinking from marriage to plain, down-to-earth Quentin because he never looked beyond her self-sufficient, independent facade to see her as a flesh-and-blood woman with weaknesses as well as strengths, with a powerful need to be known and cherished for reasons that had nothing to do with how successful she was or how skilled she could be at making intelligent conversation over coffee and brandy.

Then suddenly there was Marcello in the Casa de Fado . . . a virile, excitingly handsome man who listened when she talked, who knew her in some ways better than she knew herself. No wonder her passions had mastered her!

But now, thank heavens, she could see things as they really were. Marcello was the scientist and she was the specimen under the microscope. How lucky it was for her that she had gone sailing this afternoon. A few words from Marcello's friend had put her world back in focus.

But her emptiness persisted. It was hunger, she decided, and trailed to the kitchen for milk and cheese. Still she was dissatisfied, restless, frightened somehow. The long evening stretched dismally before her. She could write to Quentin, but, she realized sadly, she had nothing to say to him. She could dress and take a taxi to the club—but what relief would she find in sharing a table with Claudio, toying with a drink and being dragged deeper into depression by Isabel's mournful songs?

Then her eye fell on the note Isabel had left and she noticed a postscript scrawled on the other side. *White dress returns in hands of cleaner! Pay please!! Six (6) escudos. In the morning will give back your money. Cross my heart! I.*

Smiling, Gina read Isabel's scrawl again. Isabel was constantly struggling to make ends meet. She bought extravagant clothes. Her fancy car demanded huge payments, the rent on her apartment was outrageous by Portuguese standards. Fortunately Claudio bought most of her meals or she could never have survived on what the Casa de Fado paid her.

She needed a business manager . . . or a bigger income!

Restlessly, Gina retraced her steps to the living room and sank down on the couch, wondering as she settled herself among the bright cushions what the result of Isabel's audition would be.

As she had imagined, Isabel had been ecstatic when she learned Marcello had planned the entire party around her performance. It seemed almost as important to Isabel not to be indebted to Sylvia as it had been exciting to discover in what high esteem Marcello held her talent.

But almost as quickly as her mood skyrocketed, Isabel grew morose. She would have heard by now if she were to be given a chance to perform in Paris and Vienna and the other great European centers, she insisted. Nothing Gina said could persuade her that the delay could mean anything but bad news.

Isabel had taken out her frustration on Claudio, denouncing him for having mentioned the critics in the first place, and then Claudio had turned whitely furious on Gina, denouncing Marcello as a liar. Sylvia did not give parties simply because Marcello snapped his fingers. The men who had come to hear Isabel sing were Sylvia's friends, he claimed. Not Marcello's!

It had been an ugly scene all around, and Claudio had stayed away for a time, which was, Gina reflected, probably the reason he had taken Isabel away for a reconciliation. In her note Isabel might have mentioned repaying the cleaning bill the next morning because she did not intend to return to the apartment until then.

Gina's feeling of loneliness deepened. Isabel was amusing, and considering the dreary mood she was in, she would have welcomed her company.

When she heard the cleaner's knock, she even welcomed that. Securing the ties of her robe, she searched through her purse for the six *escudos*, but when she opened the door, it was not the cleaner who stood there, but Marcello, with flowers.

He wore close-fitting trousers, a navy blazer and a shirt the same color as his eyes. The bouquet he carried was comprised of late-blooming heather and early pink tulips mixed with a scattering of baby's breath and wrapped in a street vendor's cornucopia of lacy white paper.

Holding it out to her, he stepped uninvited into the room. He said gruffly, "Where have you been all afternoon?"

"Sailing." She moistened her lips, acutely conscious that she wore nothing under her robe. In spite of her recent enlightenment concerning Marcello's motives, her blood was joyously rushing through her veins. Marcello was so near she could reach out and touch him. . . .

"Did you call?"

"I left my number."

"That was days ago."

"Why didn't you ring back?"

She swallowed convulsively. "It slipped my mind."

She heard his scornful snort and felt herself drawn roughly to him. He held her in a vise-like grip, kissing her, taking her mouth with hardened lips, one hand at her nape, the other in the small of her back so that she felt the thrust of his hips through the thin robe, his taut thighs like steel, walled against her own.

He kissed her deeply, his movements against her devastatingly erotic, purposeful, his mouth insistent in its turning . . . provocative, titillating. . . .

When finally she pulled away, her breath was ragged, but she saw gratefully that he, too, was shaken. There was less of the calm assurance on his face than she had ever seen.

"I'll get a vase," she told him, pleased that she could sound so unconcerned. But in the kitchen she leaned against the counter, her eyes closed, waiting for the throbbings in her body to subside.

The kiss meant nothing, she told herself, but her heart continued to pound. When at last her hands were steady enough, she drew water to fill a glass pitcher and braced herself to face him again.

Marcello stood where she had left him, hands low on his narrow hips, but now he was composed and watchful. She made her voice sound deliberately light as she hid her face in the blossoms. "What would you have done with these if you hadn't found me at home?"

"I would have dropped them in the dustbin at the foot of the stairs."

"That would have been a pity." With her back to him, she bought time arranging the flowers, steadying herself. "But I suppose. . . ," she paused and turned around, "in five minutes someone would have come along and plucked them out again."

"Who took you sailing?"

She went to the couch. "That's none of your business."

Peeling off his coat, he threw it on a chair. "Was it anyone I know?"

"You know everyone in Lisbon, don't you? And in Estoril and Sintra?" Seeing how tense he was, she breathed easier. Suddenly she felt as she did in her shop when anxious women hung onto her every word for approval of their gown selections. Her sense of being in command, of having Marcello for the first time at a disadvantage made her smile.

"Sit down." But her moment of triumph was short-lived. The cushion beside her dipped beneath Marcello's weight. The silk robe parted and slithered away from her crossed knees and the whole glowing length of her thighs was bared suddenly in the lamplight. Swiftly she brought the cloth together again, anchoring it with damp fingers.

But the balance of power had tipped. Her near nakedness made her vulnerable, and the glittering directness of Marcello's gaze told her he appreciated that fact.

"Would you . . . ," she flitted her eyelids nervously, "would you like a glass of port?"

"Not especially."

"I would." Defiantly, she met his gaze. "Would you get it for me, please?"

Of course, he wasn't fooled. But while he was at the cabinet in the corner, she arranged herself more securely among the cushions, and when he returned she had regained her poise, though her cheeks were too bright and a feverish glow lit her eyes.

He had filled a glass for himself, too, and after he was seated beside her, she watched him tip it to his lips. The toe of his shoe restlessly tapped the table leg . . . his thumb circled the stem of the wine goblet.

A wantonness stirred ominously within her. She remembered his thumb massaging her fingertips. She recalled the caring touch of his hands on her breasts. . . .

"Cyril Crawford," she said suddenly, not aware beforehand that she meant to speak. "I went sailing with Cyril Crawford. He invited me at Sylvia's, when I was at your party."

"And you have also had lunch with Paul Pavlicka."

"How did you know?"

"Isabel told me." A faint smile twisted Marcello's lips. "Doing so gave her a great deal of pleasure."

Gina's nostrils flared. "Who have you been lunching with?"

"Lucia, except for today. A business meeting ran late. I missed lunch. I'm on my way to dinner now. Will you come with me?"

"I've had dinner." She thought fleetingly of the bite of cheese and the half glass of milk standing on the kitchen counter. If this were any man but Marcello she would get up . . . dress . . . go with him. If he hadn't kissed her . . . now she felt powerless to make any decision that would remove her for even a moment from his side. Her skin burned, her heart was pumping too fast. . . .

Marcello's gaze drifted over her. Shifting slightly, he fingered the soft collar of her robe. His hand slid around to the back of her neck, lifted her hair and let it fall again, a strand at a time. He watched it catch the light and spread across her shoulders.

"May I stay awhile?"

Gina wanted to say no. Why was she letting him do this to her again? But she heard herself from a long way off saying, "Stay if you like," and she made no move to stop his arms from coming around her. He pulled her against his chest, his hands smoothing her skin. Soft kisses fell on the curve of her cheekbone . . . at the corner of her mouth.

"How long will Isabel be gone?" he murmured.

"I don't know." All night? Panic gripped her and then gave way to dizzying desire as he turned her in his arms and brought her up along his body. A warm, spreading weakness pooled in veins. "I'm expecting the cleaner with Isabel's dress."

His lips moved against her ear. "No respectable cleaner is making deliveries this late."

He took her lips with his.

How familiar his mouth had become . . . how necessary! She kissed him back, meeting his tongue with hers, reacting jubilantly to the shock that skipped up her backbone.

He fumbled for a moment with the knot in her robe sash. Then the golden curves of her torso were reflected in the hot glow of his eyes.

Gina's breath became quick and shallow. Her fingers, with a mind of their own, opened his shirt. She bent her lips to the salty, springing curls on his chest.

Marcello said thickly, "Don't go out again with Crawford. Or with Paul."

She felt drugged. "Why?"

"I don't want you to."

"I haven't asked you not to go out with Sylvia King."

He brought her chin up, stroking the edge of her lips with his thumb, drawing with an erotic feather-touch the outline of her mouth . . . rubbing it out . . . and starting again.

"Ask me."

Her voice seemed faint, a sound belonging to someone else. "Why should I?"

His kiss answered her, a rougher kiss that hurt her mouth and lasted longer than the one before. He said huskily, "You could keep me all to yourself."

She wanted to! How could she ever have enough of this closeness, of her flesh yielding to his?

A warning note struck in her brain. Twice a fool! At Sintra he had walked away from her as if she didn't exist.

Her spine stiffened. Stirring herself, she pushed away from him, self-consciously drawing her robe closed, smoothing back her hair. In a shaky voice she asked him, "Could you really give up Sylvia?"

"In an instant. Without a backward glance." He sat up, too, regarding her with glittering eyes. On his flushed face was the listening look that both flattered and unnerved her, particularly now when she wanted him so desperately, when she could scarcely keep her hands from reaching out to the warmth of his skin.

"When someone else comes along, without a backward glance, you'll give me up, too."

He looked directly at her. "Perhaps I will. I'm offering no guarantees."

"What are you offering?"

"A chance for us to discover each other."

Her throat closed. "A few weeks of fun and games."

"Yes, that might be all there is." He took her swiftly into his arms with his body angled against her, and the silk flying away again. "Or there might be more." His voice thickened possessively. "Much, much more."

Lips trembling beneath his, she whispered, "I'm to gamble, is that it?"

"We'll both be gambling."

Swallowing, Gina fought the ecstasy of remembering his tongue invading her mouth, his moist and demanding kiss, his body so vibrantly alive molding itself to hers. Through the mad mixup of her thoughts she tried to picture Quentin. She tried to imagine feeling as out of control with him as she did now with Marcello's eyes on her.

She gave him her lips again, eagerly meeting the rough touch of his mouth. She let herself be swept along into the waiting tunnel of desire where they clung blindly to each other, limbs entangled . . . where their kisses grew deep and urgent, building, one on the other, before they turned greedy and insatiable, his lips at her breast, in the hollow of her throat.

She stopped him—mindlessly disengaging herself, coming out, she imagined numbly, from the spell he had cast—like a drowning person. Coming up for air . . . coming back to her senses . . . , she stood, a trembling column of heated flesh and rasping breath, not able to focus. In an unreliable voice that cracked at the end, she told him, "Marcello, this is too soon for me."

He answered harshly, "It wasn't too soon at Sintra."

"At Sintra you were the wise one. It's my turn now." Swiftly she wrapped her robe around her, enclosing herself again in her silk cocoon, loathing the self she saw mirrored in her mind—prim and proper Miss Thomas—putting herself away, like a prize for safekeeping. *For Quentin?* She shuddered.

But her bumping heart told her it was only a

question of time. The attraction between herself and Marcello was too strong. A moment would arrive when she would not be able to resist him.

Her gaze flew to his. His breath was still rough. His copper skin had darkened, his jaw was taut. But he gave away nothing of what he was feeling—only evidences of passion quelled too abruptly—and he was in full command of those.

Their glances locked.

He said, "We'll go to dinner. I'll pour myself another glass of port while you dress."

# Chapter Eight

Marcello took Gina back to Sintra for dinner.

In the formal dining room of his quaint house the table waited, set beautifully for two—one place at the head and the other cozily on the right. The eerie quiet of the house told her they were alone. Dry-mouthed, Gina recognized the china as Spode, the crystal as Waterford. Exquisitely striped lilies were arranged in a silver epergne flanked by candles and set on snowy linen.

"You arranged all this?" said Gina. "You got everything ready without even knowing I'd be at Isabel's when you arrived."

Marcello pulled out her chair. "I was prepared to wait."

She saw with a queasy feeling that what

had happened at Isabel's apartment was meant to have happened here, but the premature explosion of their passion had occurred there because Marcello had arrived when she was wearing nothing but a fly-away silk robe!

Here at Sintra, after wine and food and flowers all tastefully appointed—after quiet talk—Marcello would have eased her into lovemaking. Shivering, she watched him pour the wine.

But Marcello seemed intent on the meal. He served them himself, beginning with music on a sound system that brought fluid notes floating into the dining room, and then carrying from the kitchen a French meal—soup, coq au vin, fresh garden vegetables. They finished with champagne and plum tarts, and still he showed no eagerness to leave the table.

He began an account of the meeting that had kept him from lunch. Gina, lost in anxious thoughts, only half listened until she heard him say, "A delegation of farmers from Alentejo."

She relaxed a little, feeling perhaps she had misjudged him. "From your estate?"

"From what was once my estate," he corrected with a grimace. "They have petitioned me to take it over again."

"Can you do that?"

"There are ways, I suppose. But my decision was negative."

Gina remembered Cyril Crawford's mention

of the influence Marcello wielded, though his party was not in power.

"Why not? If they need you?"

He drank from the tulip-shaped glass that held his champagne before he answered. "No matter what my personal feelings are, history has passed by the *latifúndios*." His lips twitched. "Oh, we may return in another guise one day . . . as a bureaucratic version of our former selves, conveniently unrecognizable to the masses and largely powerless, I would imagine. But the norm that existed before the April 25 uprising will never be the norm again."

He concluded decisively, "It's futile to try to turn back time. One must seize whatever opportunity the moment offers—or lose it forever."

"The 'tide in the affairs of men' that Shakespeare spoke of," commented Gina, and then she warmed at his quick look of surprise.

"'If taken at the flood,'" Marcello quoted, "'leads on to fortune. Omitted, all the voyages of life are bound in shallows and in miseries.' *Julius Caesar*," he said approvingly. "You've studied the conquerors."

She smiled, suddenly shy. "I've studied the poetry of Shakespeare's dramas, but only on my own. I've had no formal instruction beyond high school."

His gaze narrowed. "Your father's fault?"

How quick he was to see through things! "His extravagance," Gina replied in a cooler tone. It still hurt to think of Christian Thomas and his friends celebrating in the Caribbean with her tuition money, but she despised for anyone else to criticize him.

"I won a scholarship," she said. "I could have worked my way through college."

"Then why didn't you?"

Nettled, she answered, "Because I chose not to." It was no business of his that her mother had begged her to stay at home and attend to the shop, that both of her parents, like opposite ends of a see-saw, had charted her course in ways she found, since she had known Marcello, difficult to justify.

She pushed back her chair. "May I tell Lucia how much I have enjoyed this delicious food?"

Marcello's smile was condescending. "I'm sure you've guessed that Lucia is no longer in the kitchen. She retires at nine no matter what is happening in Sintra. When I give large dinner parties, caterers are obliged to come in. I managed to persuade her to cook ahead this evening only because it was you whom I was bringing to dine."

He watched Gina's cheeks color from the compliment and then added, "She kindly consents to do lunches between eleven and two, but suppers she serves no later than sunset."

Was he explaining why he had hustled her back to Lisbon the last time she was here? Or had it never occurred to him how rejected she felt, how used and cast away?

"Frowning?" Marcello leaned toward her to

peer with a comic scowl at the furrow between her brows. "Is that for Lucia or for me?"

"For neither of you." Her heartbeat quickened at his closeness. "I was thinking of something unrelated."

"Can you share it?"

She shook her head, but she wished she could. She wished that everything between herself and Marcello were as uncomplicated and pleasant as the surface calm that had graced the table while they ate and talked.

"Will you tell Lucia in the morning how much I enjoyed this special treat?"

Marcello answered smoothly, "You may tell her yourself if you like."

Gina's heart flopped over. This was Marcello's technique . . . to slip up on one, to catch one unaware. "Is that what we want?" Gina tried to match his suavity. "For me to stay here with you tonight?"

"It's what I want. I can't speak for you."

A gamble. That was what he had proposed. They were to take a chance on each other, with neither of them knowing who would come out the winner, who the loser. But at least it was to his credit that he had said so frankly. And he had not promised anything—except the possibility, the vaguest kind of possibility, that the gamble might lead to discovery. Of what? Of whom?

Marcello said quietly, "What are you afraid of?"

"I'm not," she lied.

"Shakespeare spoke of the tides that lead to fortune."

"And you spoke of conquerors," she came back in a challenging tone.

His gaze hardened. "Is that how you regard me? Do you think that by bringing you here I mean to take advantage of you?"

Was he on the defensive because he was found out? Gina tried with her smile to hedge without backing down. "You have the kind of ego, I think, that demands that you take the initiative. And I can't imagine that rejection is anything you're accustomed to."

An alarming iciness crossed his face. "But you thought you might like to find out, is that it?"

"No!" Her throat tightened. "But as I said before, I think we're rushing things."

"I see."

She knew that he didn't. He had misunderstood and there was no way to let him know how she really felt without putting herself at a disadvantage. With a sinking heart she watched him push back his chair and rise.

"In that case," he said coldly, "we must give ourselves more time. I'll drive you back to Lisbon."

At the door of Isabel's apartment he said with formal courtesy that broke her heart, "Thank you for a most enlightening evening."

During the ride through the starlit night they had spoken only in monosyllables and

Gina was raging inwardly at Marcello's stubbornness by the time they climbed the stairs, but all at once she ached for him. She thought of the care with which he had planned the evening . . . of the perfectly appointed dinner, the flowers he had brought her. She thought of how she had behaved earlier, willingly inviting him to smoothe her bare skin, eagerly giving herself to his embrace.

"I know I haven't been entirely fair with you, Marcello. Another time, if we're still friends, I'll be better prepared to explain myself."

He gave a brittle laugh. "Friendship is what you want from me?"

"For now—until we've struck some kind of balance." She reached out to him with a note of pleading as he turned away. "Marcello! Tell me what you think."

One step down he paused, glancing back at her anxious eyes and parted lips.

"I think it doesn't matter—one way or the other."

As long as the heather and the tulips bloomed brightly in the glass pitcher on Isabel's sideboard, Gina held out hope that Marcello had not meant to be as brutal as he seemed when they parted.

But by the end of the week when the faded bouquet finally found its way to the dustbin, she was suffering too much to fool herself any longer. Also, she was furious. One chance after another had been given her to turn her back on Marcello, but instead she had allowed the reverse to happen—twice!

Common sense had warned her, past experience had preached, and still she had let her emotions run rampant. She had closed her eyes to everything and lost herself in Marcello's arms, in the swirling passion his touch instantly aroused.

Now she was paying for it.

He had even warned her. He offered no guarantees, he said. Without a backward glance he might forget her.

On Saturday morning she packed her bags and announced to Isabel that she was taking the train to Beja and would hire a car from there to take her to the farm.

"Are you going because of Marcello?" Isabel shrieked.

"Because of me." Gina managed a wan smile. "I've hardly seen Emilio and Valentina."

"But what will you do for company in the middle of grain fields with no one but them?"

"Rest, read. I found an English bookstore today."

"You prefer books when you could be looking into Marcello's eyes?" Isabel was incredulous. "Aren't you in love with him?"

"I'm in love with Quentin!" Gina knew she was overreacting, but she couldn't stop herself. "I'm going to marry him, you know!"

Isabel's black eyes popped. "How can you do that when he writes such stupid letters?"

"Isabel! You've read my mail?"

"Only one tiny little peek!" Isabel flew to her side. "What woman can resist a love letter? But this is not what you receive." She poked her lips out scornfully. "All your Quentin writes about is court docks!"

"Dockets!" Gina corrected firmly. "He is a distinguished lawyer who takes an active interest in his work."

Isabel answered sadly, "Quentin is a man with no soul."

The train ride to Beja took less than three hours. By nightfall Gina was sitting at Valentina's table, listening to her and Emilio talk and already feeling restless.

What was Marcello doing? But immediately she despised herself for caring. As soon as the supper dishes were dried, she pleaded exhaustion and took herself off to her room to write a long letter to Quentin. In detail she told him about the sights of Lisbon and the beauties of the farm, but in the concluding paragraph when she mentioned that she would soon be home, her pen faltered.

How could she go back to Nantucket knowing she would never see Marcello again? A hole seemed to open in space and she felt herself falling through it toward endless, meaningless days that stretched out to the end of her life.

Without even signing her letter, she turned out the light and climbed into bed.

\* \* \*

The mornings on the Alentejo plains were sunlit and crisp, and Gina trudged the winding lanes that led through grainfields, grateful that exercise and fresh air helped keep her mind off things less agreeable.

But again and again she was reminded of Marcello. The *Alentejanos* were a friendly people, but most were far less prosperous than Emilio, and she could not help thinking of Marcello's comment that they needed leadership to succeed. Whenever she passed a large estate house fallen into disrepair, she wondered if it might be Marcello's. She tried to picture him as a grubby little boy on the flat plains searching for a place to hide, but invariably she saw him as the sensuous, compelling man he had become.

She had been unwise, she soon discovered, bringing novels to this place. Their plots only set her thinking of her own tangled life, and she lay in the hammock on Emilio's porch and sightlessly turned the pages.

A week passed. Isabel came for a day and a night. When she mentioned Marcello, Emilio pricked up his ears, and an argument ensued. Emilio launched heatedly into an attack against Marcello and men like him who had ruthlessly dealt with their countrymen.

"Then why have his tenants petitioned him to resume control of his land?" Gina put in, amazed that she could defend Marcello, but not so amazed as Emilio who overcame his astonishment by blustering heatedly. No such offer had been forthcoming, he was certain, but if it had been, Gina could rest assured Marcello would have snatched it up.

In the flurry of Isabel's departure no further mention was made of Marcello, and Gina was relieved, but at the same time she felt more alive than she had since she had taken the train out of Lisbon.

Another week went by and then one sunny morning when she was halfway to the village to mail a letter, she saw a man on horseback approaching. Though he was far down the road, Gina knew at once that it was Marcello. There was no disguising the erectness of his body, the proud carriage of his head. Automatically she glanced about for a place to hide, but like the youthful Marcello she found none. There was only stubble as far as the eye could see.

In a few minutes he was at her side, gazing down at her with that listening look that haunted all her dreams. Only his smile was absent.

"So here you are," he said curtly.

Where else would she be? she wanted to shout. He had driven her out of Lisbon with his cruelty! But her heart was hammering and she was drinking in the sight of him like some poor starved thing dying on a desert.

"From what Emilio told me," he said, "I thought you might be halfway to America."

She was too surprised not to show it. "You've been to the farm?"

123

"I telephoned." And then at last there was his smile. "It isn't Mars, you know."

"What did he say? Did he tell you I'd gone home?"

"He said you weren't there. But he made it sound final enough that I thought perhaps you had shortened your visit."

"Why would I do that?" she said stiffly.

The corners of his mouth twitched again. "Obviously you didn't."

He got off his horse and stood beside her. She had the impression that he was taller. It was his boots, she decided, and felt pale and wobbly in his shadow, like a patient whose recovery from a ghastly illness was still uncertain.

In a quavering voice she said, "Have you come here to take over your estate again?"

He laughed. "Of course not. I told you I wasn't considering that."

"I told that to Emilio, but seeing you, I thought I might have to eat my words."

"You defended me to your uncle?"

She flushed. "Only incidentally. Some of his attitudes are so bigoted I couldn't resist." Immediately she felt disloyal and added quickly, "But don't misunderstand me. I'm very fond of him."

"I'm fond of him too, except when he talks of things he knows nothing about." Marcello's keen gaze inspected her. "You're thinner. Hasn't the country life agreed with you?"

Devil! she thought, but she answered evenly, "I love it here."

"More than in Lisbon?"

"It's different from Lisbon."

"You've been down to the coast, of course."

But she hadn't, and she rubbed the horse's nose, feeling awkward and stupid. "I've been taking it easy."

His gaze sharpened. "A little of that goes a long way."

She realized suddenly how right he was, how bored she had been for days on end, almost in a stupor. "You haven't told me what you're doing here."

"I rejected the invitation to reclaim my land, but I did agree to consult on one or two matters. I'll be on my way back to the city this evening." His gaze settled on her lips. "May I give you a lift if you're ready to return?"

She almost refused, simply on the grounds of being contrary, but she had a little time left before her return ticket to America was valid. She couldn't envision spending it on the plains of Alentejo. Besides, Marcello had already opened all her old wounds. What other damage could he do if she rode with him?

"When are you leaving?"

"Whenever you say."

"I could be ready soon after lunch, I suppose. Shall we make it two o'clock?"

"Two it is." He swung back up on his horse. "May I give you a lift now?"

"No, thank you." Her thoughts were racing so, she could scarcely remember where she was headed. Was she behaving stupidly again? She had gained a sensible perspective, surely, in two weeks away from him. She was confident that she was herself again—competent, in charge of her life.

Gina watched as he turned in his saddle and lifted an arm. She waved in return and gazed after him until he was only a speck at the end of the road. He was different, too, she decided, and tried to ignore the wind that blew through her heart. They were both different. The fire that had burned between them was ashes now. She had nothing to fear from Marcello. Nothing except the desolation that gripped her.

# Chapter Nine

Gina had heard from her mother about the charm of Portugal's Algarve region—an irregular strip of land that bordered the southernmost edge, and she wondered, when Marcello announced that he was driving her to see it before they returned to Lisbon, why she hadn't gone there before. It was only a short distance from Emilio's farm. She could have easily borrowed the car.

Marcello questioned her about her lack of interest in the coast as soon as they were underway. "How could you resist going to take a look at the ocean when for a month you were only a stone's throw away?"

"For two weeks," she corrected, but her heart turned over. Did her absence seem longer to him? Had he suffered a little, too?

But if he had, he gave no other sign, and, as they rode along, Gina glanced enviously at his craggy profile. He appeared never to have suffered from anything. The Algarve light turned his copper skin to bronze, and he seemed bursting with health and virility as he praised the terrain.

Soon Gina was praising it, too, infected by his enthusiasm and charmed by the miles of pale sand and the white sugar-cube houses that rose from slopes brilliantly filled with scarlet geraniums.

Back from the water were the almond trees Marcello had spoken of, and on the opposite hand, cavorting in the surf, was an amazing congregation of Swedish polar bears.

"It's a magic place, isn't it?" murmured Gina when they sat down to an early dinner in a white-washed restaurant where the tables were set with vases of fresh carnations and aquarium tanks lined the walls.

"It's one of the few unspoiled places left in the world," Marcello answered. "Mountains cut it off for generations and the rest of Portugal forgot about it. Until the bridge was built in Lisbon, making it accessible at last, only the English bothered to vacation here."

Gina looked out at the imposing hotels towering on the beach. "They must be a bit resentful now that their hideaway has been discovered."

"Perhaps." Marcello lifted a forkful of his filet of sole and chewed appreciatively. In a moment he said, "But in my view, the English are the most civilized people in the world. Certainly they harbor the least ill will." He smiled suddenly. "I think they would be delighted that we're here absorbing the splendor."

His look had the effect of the sun coming out. Up to that point, he had been courteous, but aloof. Now Gina glimpsed something of the Marcello who made her heart sing, and she smiled back.

"Thank you for bringing me here."

"Don't think we've finished seeing everything," he warned. "There are other wonders to behold. And you said you are interested in fishermen's sweaters for your shop. As long as we're here, we might as well have a look around for those."

"Marcello," Gina took a deep breath, "why are we here?"

"What?"

"When we said good night several weeks ago you made it rather plain that you didn't care whether or not we ever saw each other again."

"I said I didn't think it mattered whether we were friends or not."

"Have you changed your mind?"

He gave her a speculative grin. "Would I be here if I hadn't?"

Gina didn't know. Would he? He had rung up the farm looking for her, but what did that prove? Isabel could have begged him, too.

And certainly he had enjoyed his brief clash with Emilio when he had come to pick her up. The barbed remarks he and her uncle had exchanged had provided a topic for spirited conversation all the way to the coast. Perhaps he had used her only as a means of needling Emilio about the changing tempers of the plains farmers.

But whatever Marcello's motives, he was too engaging a tour guide for Gina to think for long about anything except the Algarve's enchantments. They wandered around until long after twilight, and it was very late when they finally arrived at Isabel's darkened apartment.

"Her show was over long ago. Why isn't she here?" asked Gina when repeated knockings failed to rouse Isabel. The key was not in its customary place in a hanging pot of fuchsia.

"Well, you can't sit here on the steps waiting until she comes back," said Marcello evenly. "*If* she comes back. You'd better come along with me."

"To Sintra?" Gina caught her breath. "I can't do that."

"To my apartment here in Lisbon." Marcello took her arm.

"I can't go there, either!"

"Would you rather stay in a hotel for five or six hours when I have a perfectly comfortable room available? Quite separate from mine," he added bluntly.

There was just enough contempt in his

voice to make Gina feel ashamed. "If you're sure I won't be putting you out."

"Not at all." He smiled sardonically. "There's nothing I wouldn't do for a friend."

When Gina woke, it was nearly noon. Marcello's apartment on the tree lined Avenida da Liberdade was well-insulated from the noise of traffic, and she had slept more soundly than she had in weeks.

She decided at once to dress rather than appear again in front of Marcello in her infamous silk robe, but on the way to the closet she discovered a note shoved under the door that led to the hall. Marcello had already gone out, the dark slanting script explained. Breakfast was in the oven.

Still in her robe, she wandered out to inspect the apartment she had only glimpsed on her arrival. From the dark leather chairs in the living room to the steel cabinets in the kitchen it was definitely a bachelor's quarters, with everything designed for minimum care. No servant was on hand, so apparently when Marcello stayed in town, he looked after his own needs, and the needs of his guests. He had set a place for her in a sunny spot at the table. Freshly squeezed orange juice was poured in a crystal wine goblet and when she opened the warm oven, a lidded casserole revealed a sausage and egg dish that gave off a heavenly aroma—and hot biscuits, besides.

Marcello had prepared an American breakfast for her!

As Gina ate she wondered how much time Marcello had spent in her country. It was a topic they had never discussed. Wistfully she thought that there was so much she didn't know about him, so much she would never know. She still wasn't sure why he had looked her up at Emilio's farm and offered her passage back to Lisbon, but she was certain of one thing: Marcello was no longer interested in her in a romantic way.

In the hours they had spent together he had behaved toward her as he would have toward any other visitor with whom he was casually acquainted. He had been a thoughtful, entertaining host, but if anything, the distance between them seemed to have widened after she had questioned him. When he had let her into the apartment, they had shared a brief nightcap in the study while they examined his collection of jazz records. Then he had shown her the bedroom suite, where the light switches were, and after that he had disappeared down the opposite end of the hall.

The tension she had worked up in anticipation of fending off at least a good-night kiss, she had had to work off in an hour of restless tossing, and then she had fallen into a sleep so sound that even his breakfast preparations had not aroused her.

Uneasily examining her feelings in the uncompromising light of day, Gina set about washing up the breakfast things. But almost at once the doorbell sounded.

Her heart flew up in her throat. Had Marcello forgotten his key? She was asking for trouble opening the door for him half-naked again! But there was no getting around that now.

The bell sounded another time before she could reach the entry hall and again before she finally got the latch off—and then when the door swung open at last, Sylvia King sailed in.

She stopped short when she saw Gina in her nightclothes, a look of total astonishment sweeping her face. "You! What are you doing here?"

A sudden perversity seized Gina. The explanation she might have offered someone else died on her tongue. "I spent the night here," she answered calmly. "Are you looking for Marcello?"

"I'm certainly not looking for you!"

"Obviously. Well, I'm sorry. Marcello had to go out." Gina put her hand on the doorknob. "I'll tell him you dropped by."

"I thought you had gone back to Nantucket."

"Really? Who told you that?"

"Whoever did is plainly a liar!" The careful courtesy Sylvia had shown on the other occasions when they had met was so blatantly absent in this exchange that Gina found herself grinning.

"Would you like a cup of coffee or a biscuit? I'm just finishing my breakfast."

"It's noon," Sylvia answered haughtily. "Marcello and I have a luncheon engagement."

"Then make yourself comfortable. I'll just go and finish tidying up."

Gina had managed to keep her tone objective, but inwardly she was shaken. Marcello was still seeing Sylvia, apparently on a regular basis, the details of which she preferred not to contemplate. But at least the woman who was trailing her toward the kitchen hadn't been given a key to the apartment!

"Look here," Sylvia planted herself firmly in front of Gina. "I let it go when you were in Lisbon before and went out with Marcello. He has a streak of the bumpkin in him and enjoys treks to mountaintops and picnics in bizarre places, which I abhor. But I will not have you going to bed with him!"

Gina said coolly, "Are you in charge of Marcello's sleeping arrangements?"

"I am the only woman of consequence in Marcello's life!"

"I see. Whose opinion is that? Yours or his?" Gina saw the flash of red that swept up Sylvia's porcelain throat and added dryly, "Never mind. I know the answer—or I wouldn't be here."

She had scored a direct hit, she saw. Sylvia's face exploded in color. "You've gone too far! I knew the minute I laid eyes on you that you were a cheap shop girl who would stoop to anything. Wait until I tell Quentin what his precious fianceé is up to."

"And what is that?" Gina asked without betraying that Sylvia had also hit her mark.

"Snaring Marcello, obviously!"

"Then why am I any cheaper than you?" Gina clenched her hands into fists to stop their trembling and hid them in the folds of her robe. "If you wore a printed sign, you couldn't say any clearer that you're out to snare Marcello yourself."

Sylvia's pale eyes flashed angrily. "I'm glad at least that you understand that much! It might be well if you understand something else, too. Even if Marcello falls madly in love with you—which is preposterous, of course—there's no place for a woman of your sort in his life."

Her lips twisted into an unbecoming sneer. "Your mother was nothing more than an Alentejo peasant, and your father was a scoundrel. With your upbringing and background, you could never fit into the cosmopolitan life Marcello leads."

Rage unleashed Gina's tongue. "Marcello won't be leading that life any longer. He's bored to death with nightclubs and gaudy mansions like yours maintained simply to impress people."

She knew she was speaking recklessly, treading on perilously thin ground, but the words continued to tumble out on their own volition. "When Marcello and I are married, Sintra will be our home and the door will never be open to you or any other shallow,

superficial social climber from your cosmopolitan set."

"Married!" Sylvia shook with rage. "You
and Marcello? You're insane!"

Gina's eyes blazed back at her. "Am I? Shall
we wait and see?"

"I am not waiting for anything!" Sylvia
lifted her Patrician nose. "You may tell Marcello when he has rid himself of you, he can
call me. Until then, he needn't bother."

After Sylvia stormed out of the apartment,
Gina sat down shakily at the kitchen table.
Had she actually told that terrible woman
that she and Marcello were to be married?
Had her subconscious been harboring that
incredible idea ever since the white peacock
had shed part of its tail at her feet?

*Marcello's wife . . . at home in Sintra.*

She shut her eyes and saw the garden blazing with color, the castle in the hazy distance.
She smelled the sweet air and pictured herself
in Marcello's arms, not struggling against his
virile embrace, not worrying about the damage an irresponsible, romantic hedonist could
inflict . . . but languishing there, secure in
the love of the man she adored.

It was heaven.

But it was also without substance. Opening
her eyes, Gina took hold of herself, self-control
tightening her loosely smiling lips. Marcello
was not capable of love, and she was too
sensible and too well-acquainted with the
pain her father had caused her mother to ever

seriously consider marriage to such a man. Quentin Bromley was the man she was going to marry as soon as she could get over this foolish infatuation with Marcello. Actually it would be a relief to get back to Nantucket and into the sane routine of a life with Quentin. She was worn out with oscillating emotions. She was exhausted from battling unseemly desires . . . from yearning for the taste of Marcello's lips.

The weak feeling she had learned to dread swept over her. Somehow she had to rid herself of this nonsensical sexual attraction that had her going three ways at once.

But was running away the answer? Gina thought bleakly. With hundreds of miles between her and Marcello, how would she ever get him out of her system, out of her dreams? She had run away to Alentejo and there on the plains he had grown bigger than life. She had almost devoured him when she set eyes on him again.

Desperately she begged the white walls of the kitchen for an answer, but their only response was to echo the ticking of the clock. She finished drying the dishes and went to her room to dress.

Gina was dressed and setting her bags in the entry hall when Marcello's key turned in the lock. Her heart came up in her throat, and she despised herself for dawdling when she could have been halfway across the city in a taxi. Now she was trapped with only two choices:

she could brazen out the encounter—or jump from a window!

Breathlessly, she waited while he opened the door. She imagined that he would see the torment she was suffering written all over her face, but when he caught sight of her standing stiffly beside the umbrella stand, his only reaction appeared to be relief.

"Good, you're still here. I thought you might have gone over to Isabel's by now, but when I swung around that way the place was still locked." A trace of cynicism edged his voice. "I suppose she's tucked away in Estoril with her friend."

Gina bristled. "Your friend from Estoril came knocking a short time ago." How long would it be before Sylvia spread the word that Gina expected to marry him? "She came to keep a lunch date she said, but she couldn't wait."

Marcello scowled. "Sylvia said she had a lunch date with me?"

Would it be better to tell him herself what ridiculous things had been said? But how on earth to begin? She licked her lips. "We quarreled."

Marcello regarded her intently. "You and Sylvia. What about?"

"You."

"I see."

"She said some unfortunate things." Gina swallowed nervously. "So did I." Pausing, she braced herself for further questions, but instead he looked down at her bags and said,

"Where are you off to? You can't go to Isabel's, you know."

She had been too occupied with framing what she meant to say next to realize that she was stranded. "There's a hotel in Isabel's neighborhood. I'll stay there until she comes back."

"The place is a fleabag," he said so decisively that Gina surprised herself by laughing.

"Have you ever spent a night there?"

"I don't have to, to know that it isn't the sort of lodging for you. But never mind, I have an idea."

She could tell from the exaggeratedly casual way he spoke that whatever he was about to suggest was not as unpremeditated as he pretended. Instinctively, she tensed. "What?"

"Since you didn't find your fishermen's sweaters in Algarve, I think we should run up the coast to Nazare and see what's available there."

"Nazare?" She stared at him blankly, her heartbeat accelerating. Then this wasn't to be the end of it? He wasn't simply going to drop out of her life forever.

He took in her stare and the skin at his eye corners crinkled with the same amusement his voice held. "Surely you've heard of Nazare. It's one of Portugal's more attractive spots."

"Of course I've heard of it. But I was thinking . . ."

"Of what?"

"Marcello . . ." If they were going to go on

seeing each other then she could not put off telling him what she had told Sylvia. "About the quarrel I mentioned."

A look of annoyance crossed his face. "If we're going, we ought to get on the road."

"There's something you ought to know before we start out."

"Spare me the details."

"Even though they concern you?"

"Most especially if they concern me." His tone grew brisk and he reached for her bags. "I'll stow these in the car and come back for a few things of my own."

"Wait. . . ." Every nerve in her body tingled. "Nazare isn't that far is it? Won't we be back within a few hours?"

"What's the point in hurrying?" he answered smoothly. "The village is delightful and as long as we're going, we ought to see everything, don't you agree? The hotel there is known for its fine food, and you won't want to miss the fishing boats."

He hoisted her bags and turned toward the door. "We might even go up as far as Porto and have a look at my vineyards."

"Marcello, you're talking about being gone for days!"

He lifted his dark brows. "Yes . . . why not?"

"I can't just go running off with you." Her thoughts flew in a dozen directions. "Isabel won't know where I am."

"Then she won't be worried. She'll think you're still at the farm."

"She might call there. Valentina would be frantic if I simply disappeared."

He set the bags down. "Call the farm and tell her you're with me."

"No."

He said coolly, "Are you tied to your aunt's apron strings?"

"I respect her feelings—and Emilio's."

"Gina . . ." He took her by the shoulders in a grip so firm that it robbed her of her breath. "I've asked you to go to Nazare with me, and to Porto. I'll take no for an answer only if you don't want to go."

"It isn't that. . . ."

"No other reason counts," he told her sternly. "I've issued an invitation, friend to friend." His blue eyes sparked with challenge. "Your part is to say yes or no—but to stand on your own two feet when you say it."

"Yes," she answered faintly.

A glitter of triumph deepened the penetration of his gaze. "I'll get a few things together. I'll be with you in a minute."

# Chapter Ten

Riding up the coast toward Nazare, Gina fought a new sense of unreality. What kind of insanity was this, shutting herself up in a car for miles with Marcello in such close proximity, agreeing to let the journey drag out for days, purposely torturing herself every time she thought of the opportunities they would have for making love?

Madness! There was no other name for it.

But gradually she calmed down. Marcello was unusually reserved, speaking only when spoken to and not bothering, as he ordinarily did, to point out the special attractions of the countryside. Perhaps he was sorry, too, that he had let himself in for hours of travel with a woman who insisted on being only his friend.

Or perhaps he was taking revenge on her for

having run off to Alentejo when his ego demanded that he be the one to break off with
her. He had resented her suggestion that he
could not accept rejection. Maybe in the next
few days he meant to set her up for his own
form of rejection!

But glancing at his chiseled profile outlined
against the blue sky, she found it difficult to
believe that he would hurt her so callously.
Her eyes followed the outline of his lips and
she recalled their burning intensity. She
thought of his warm, muscled body pressed
against hers, and once again desire racked
her.

Good! she thought fiercely. Maybe burn-out
was the cure. These days of enforced proximity might be exactly what was needed to exor-
cise Marcello's hold on her. There was a limit
to every human emotion. You wept until tears
ceased to flow, and then you wiped your eyes
dry and got on with living again. Desire must
have its limits, too. If it went unfulfilled for
too long, then surely it diminished. Perhaps it
even became repugnant!

She looked hopefully across at Marcello,
trying to imagine how she would feel, purged
of longing for him. Could a time ever come
when she wouldn't crave his embrace?

He felt her looking at him and smiled, and
she looked away quickly, fearing he might
read her thoughts.

It was late afternoon when they arrived in
Nazare, and Gina was at once captivated by

143

the quaintness of the village. All its social life seemed centered at the beach where groups of women draped in black shawls waited on the buttery sand for the return of the fishermen.

"It's like a sewing circle!" Gina whispered as she and Marcello strolled past the chattering females busily engaged with embroidery and mending while they gossiped. Beneath the somber cloth that draped their shoulders, she glimpsed bright-colored garments of a type rarely worn by Portuguese women, and she commented on that.

Marcello, who himself seemed more relaxed now that she was enthusiastically endorsing their arrival, had an answer for her.

"The inhabitants of Nazare consider themselves descendants of the phoenicians—even their boats are styled along that line—and they follow a set of customs peculiar to this one particular area. Here . . ." He pointed out a low, wooden bench off to one side of the huddled groups of women and suggested that they sit there. "We'll get a fine view of the boats coming in and you'll see that their use of color isn't restricted merely to clothing."

Within a few minutes Gina realized what he meant. Across the flat sea a high-prowed boat appeared, and then another and another until the horizon was streamered like a rainbow by the oncoming vessels. As they drew closer, Gina could see that their historically shaped hulls were striped in brilliant yellows, greens, blues, and reds. On the bows of some, enormous eyes were painted.

"To assist in locating the fish," Marcello told her, smiling.

The fishermen themselves were gaily bedecked in Scottish plaid trousers and shirts of startling contrast. Oxen were led up, yoked in pairs, and while the women and children looked on, the animals were harnessed to the prows of the boats. When the word was given, the oxen dragged the vessels ashore.

"Now it's everyone's turn to work," said Marcello when the huge nets of silvery fish were emptied. All sizes and both sexes of Nazare onlookers began to haul them away in every conceivable sort of container.

"The *varinas*, the fishwives," he told Gina, "will hawk their wares from door to door. The fish that aren't sold will be dried in the sun on those racks. The women who aren't engaged in selling or drying will be mending the nets at sunrise and then the whole process will start again."

While they were having their dinner at the hotel where they were to stay that evening, Gina questioned him further and learned that the colorful spectacle she had witnessed on the beach and the one promised for in the morning, when the families gathered to see their men off, were often tinged with tragedy.

"Portuguese fishermen risk their lives every time they go to sea," said Marcello. "The surf can be suicidal here."

"Then why do they do it?"

Marcello shrugged. "Why do birds fly? Men

have fished from Nazaré for centuries. It's the only life they know, the only one that holds any meaning for them."

Sobered, Gina followed him out onto the terrace of the hotel to watch the sturdy fishermen stalking past in their checkered shirts and red berets and with their mascot dogs following closely at their heels.

"I have a feeling for this place," she said quietly.

At her side Marcello struck a match to one of the dark little cigars he sometimes smoked. "Perhaps your ancestors originated here."

She shook her head and then held herself tensely as he draped an arm over her shoulder. "They were all from Alentejo. All farmers." She relaxed a little when Marcello seemed only to be sheltering her from the wind. In a moment she said, "I suppose in a way Sylvia was right. She called my mother a peasant."

Marcello's dark brows jumped together. "What reason did she have to say that? I can't imagine she meant it kindly."

"Peasantry has unflattering connotations at best," Gina agreed, "but I provoked her a bit before she blurted it out. I guess I can't blame her too much."

When she saw that Marcello was listening intently, she ventured a step further. "I opened the door in my nightgown."

"Oh, I see. Then it's not hard to guess what she thought."

"I'm afraid I encouraged those thoughts. She annoys me, you know. She always has."

"Ever since she announced your engagement to Quentin in the Casa de Fado."

Gina looked away from his slightly scornful smile. "She researched my background. I knew she would. She knew all about my father."

"Then she knows more than I do," Marcello said quietly.

Gina looked around in surprise. "The first time we talked I told you what sort of man he was."

"You told me what happened to him—not how you felt toward him." Marcello put out his cigar. "You don't hate him as you pretend, and yet you seem to blame him for all sorts of things that have happened to you." His arm slid down around her waist and he turned her toward him. "Life isn't that simple, you know. We create most of our problems for ourselves."

If he meant to rub salt in her wounds, he was surely succeeding. "That's easy for you to say!" she flashed back at him. "I can't think you've ever had anything really earthshaking to deal with. Everything has pretty much been handed to you . . . the cork groves, the vineyards."

"Some of it has been taken away," he answered mildly. Before she could reply, he added, "It isn't what happens to us, good or bad, that matters so much. It's how we perceive it, how we react to it that counts. That's what makes us who we are."

"I don't think I deserve a lecture from you."

"Perhaps I'm lecturing myself as well." He lowered his head until his lips were almost touching hers. "Perhaps I'm saying, 'Marcello, you have in your arms a woman who keeps secrets, a woman who fears her own emotions. But the important thing is, you have her in your arms.'"

He kissed her then, an ardent, exploring kiss that awakened responses that had only intensified during weeks of being away from him. The familiar melting sensation coursed through her, and she had all she could do to keep him from knowing how deeply she cared for him.

When he released her at last, Gina said shakily, "This was supposed to have been a friendly excursion."

She heard his low chuckle. "Wasn't that a friendly kiss?"

Old fears rose like ghosts. "Are we headed back down the road we came up?"

"I hope so," he said, taking her in his arms again. "Gina, Gina . . . ," his lips moved along her cheekbone. "What is it? What makes you so skittish?"

"What makes you think that with one kiss you can wipe out three weeks of ignoring me?"

"You were wary before I ignored you—or else I never would have." His arms tightened around her. "It can't be that Bromley fellow in Nantucket, can it? You can't seriously be thinking of marrying him."

Gina's heart stopped. So that was it. That was why he had brought her here, to prove himself a better man than Quentin! Apparently for Marcello, competition ranked in the same category with rejection—he couldn't cope with either one. All at once she was furious at him.

"Why can't I be thinking of marrying Quentin? He's a reliable, trustworthy man who will make an excellent husband! I expect the wedding will be in the spring."

"I see." With a suddenness that left her shaken, he took his arms away. "Forgive me for forcing my attentions on you. I've been a trifle slow in grasping your pleas for friendship."

His tone was so void of emotion that it seemed to Gina he was almost in shock. Her mouth went dry. Had she been mistaken about the whole thing? "Marcello . . ."

But his clipped response cut her off. "You must be quite uncomfortable here with me. We'll return to Lisbon tomorrow—or tonight if you'd rather."

"I don't care what we do!" Her voice was thick with unshed tears. "But if you're leaving it up to me, then I say finish what you started when you brought me here!"

His hollow answer struck her like a slap. "Whatever you say."

\* \* \*

When Gina woke up in the morning to the cries of the *varinas* making their rounds, the sun was barely up. From her window she could see the families gathered around the nets on the beach and the brightly colored boats about to be launched again.

Yesterday she had pictured herself with Marcello enjoying this interesting spectacle, but when they had parted shortly after their quarrel, no plans had been made for today.

She pulled on a skirt and sweater, tied a scarf over her hair to keep it in place in the wind, and set out by herself toward the beach. Spotting the bench they had occupied the evening before, she settled on it, but the fascinating activity taking place before her did not absorb her attention.

She ached all over from her misunderstanding with Marcello. What a tangled mess their lives had become! Why couldn't she simply have told him the truth—that her feelings were ambivalent because she had grown up distrusting a handsome, charming man? Why couldn't she have confessed what she knew now was a fact: she would never marry Quentin. He was trustworthy and reliable . . . and boring! Having known Marcello, she could never spend the rest of her life discussing writs of habeas corpus with Quentin.

Suddenly she was aware of Marcello standing beside her.

"I—I didn't realize you were up," she stammered.

His eyes were colder than the chill wind that cut through Gina. "I've been making inquiries about the sweaters for your shop. A woman several miles beyond the village takes orders on consignment. If you like, we can stop to see her on our way to Porto. That is, if you still want to go."

"Do you?"

"You might find it worthwhile. The harvesting of the grapes is not an ordinary sight."

Gina cared nothing for the grapes or for seeing another city. No matter what the cost, she wanted to be sheltered in Marcello's arms, she wanted his heartbeat under her ear, her mouth on his. "I'll leave it to you to decide," she said.

He shrugged. "There is always business I can attend to at the vineyards."

Business! He was more like Quentin than she thought! But time was running out. Marcello believed she was marrying Quentin in the spring. When he took her back to Lisbon, she would never see him again.

She rose abruptly and in a stiffly formal tone said, "I should like very much to see your vineyards. You're kind to invite me."

Something dark and inscrutable showed in his eyes. Her heart took a wild leap. Pain? But in an instant it was gone.

With equal formality he answered, "Then we'll leave as soon as we've had breakfast."

On the drive up the coast, Gina turned over in her mind the wretched impasse she had reached with Marcello. Earlier, while they were having lunch—a perfectly ordinary Portuguese lunch of soup and fish, potatoes and radishes—she had watched Marcello squeezing lemon over his fish, his strong bronzed hand manipulating the thin rind, and all at once she had realized as clearly as if it were branded on her brain that she could have no life separate from this man.

It made no difference if he was a carbon copy of Christian Thomas. She could be no more miserable with him than without him, and actually she had no choice. Without meaning to, without even knowing when it happened, she had fallen helplessly in love with him.

To have made this vital discovery at such a mundane moment seemed to Gina symbolic of the wrong course their whole relationship had taken and her eyes filled with tears.

Looking up, Marcello saw her distress and thought the lemon juice had squeezed into her eyes. She let him think that, accepting his apology, but all the time she was desperate to throw her arms around him. She loved his hands, even his fingers dabbing at her tears. Everything about him was precious to her.

But she said nothing, not having the slightest idea where to begin, what to confess first, and more importantly, not knowing if after she confessed she found his feelings not the same as hers, how she would go on living.

Now she concentrated her gaze on the

winding road that overlooked the sea and thought how hopeless it all was. He hadn't touched her since lunch, and every nerve in her body was crying out. If he cared for her as she cared for him he would know that, wouldn't he? Across the leather seat he would sense the messages she was sending him.

Then suddenly he turned off the main road. She saw the name of a village flash past, and she jumped as if she were scalded. Perhaps he *had* gotten her message! "Where are we going?"

His clipped answer punctured her hope. "To a bullfight. No one should leave Portugal without having seen one."

*Leave Portugal.* Then he had already crossed her off. She said numbly, "I'm not sure if I can handle the bloodshed."

To her surprise, he laughed. "If you faint, I promise to revive you."


As it happened, almost no blood was shed. A few drops from the *banderillas*, and that was all. Gina had somehow not known that the bull is never killed in a Portuguese bull ring; up until the end of the fight, she sat tensely beside Marcello, miserable enough with her own problems and dreading the debacle she expected to take place before her.

Dazedly she watched the brass band that opened the proceedings and the entrance of a corps of brilliantly costumed men who paraded around the ring and bowed and scraped with their tricorn hats. After that there were horsemen and finally the bull and a lone man on foot, carrying a cape.

Gina squeezed her eyes nearly shut while the men on horseback stuck in their *banderillas* to anger the bull. But then to her amazement, a comic free-for-all began, instead of slaughter. The dazzlingly costumed men who had first entered the ring appeared again, this time like a team of circus clowns, and they at once set about pitting their wits against the snorting animal. One of them caught hold of its tail and swished it; another hung onto the neck for dear life and still another ran around in circles echoing the raucous noises and nonsense of the others and occasionally peeling off into a cartwheel.

When the animal was finally exhausted, the crowd cheered and whistled through their teeth and joyously drained out of the bleachers.

"That's all there is?" said Gina, blinking. "They aren't going to cut off the poor bull's ears?"

Marcello's dark brows rose. "No, of course not. Is that what's had you so terrified?" Then he took her by the hand and bought her a chocolate-coated ice cream on a stick and presented it to her as if she were a child who had behaved with exceptional courage.

When they were on the road again, Marcello said in the same protective way, "It never occurred to me that you might not know everything about Portuguese bullfights since you are half-Portuguese yourself."

"The same as you." Gina had not thought before of their having that common bond.

Neither, it seemed, had Marcello. He answered without jest, "Together we make one whole citizen."

They stared at each other until his attention was required to keep the car from running off the road, and afterward they were quiet, each lost in thought.

Porto was a garden land of vivid flowers and a warren of ancient buildings that came straight down to the water and fascinated Gina with the way they appeared to be stacked one on top of the other. But she and Marcello did not linger in the city as she had expected. His vineyards were an hour's drive to the east, and they paused only long enough to eat a delicious dinner in an elegant old castle turned into a *pousada*.

By nightfall Marcello had engaged rooms for them in a cozy little inn. Over a nightcap in the bar off the lobby, he explained to Gina the method by which the grapes were harvested and then turned into huge metal cylinders where they were processed.

Gina's expression clouded as he talked. "Aren't the grapes stamped by human feet any longer?"

He smiled at her look of disappointment. "Only in rare instances. Does that tradition appeal to you?"

"Oh, yes, it does!"

"Then you must see it done. In one of my vineyards this is still the custom. We pass right by it. We can easily stop."

They left early in the morning, traveling along narrow roads where carts pulled by oxen were mounded high with the dewy purple fruit. Marcello stopped several times to consult with overseers while Gina remained in the car, enthralled with the activity around her.

Every square inch of land that climbed the sheer banks rising from the river was covered with grape-laden vines. Workers moved among the thick growth, plucking the clustered globes to the rhythm of drums and flutes, while others hoisted the filled baskets onto their shoulders and trudged with them toward waiting ox carts.

All over the valley hung the fragrance of the grapes—a rich, sensuous perfume that filled Gina's nostrils and sent a quiver of arousal trailing along her spine. Feeling wanton and not caring that she did, she recognized that she was associating bacchanalia, the passionate pagan history of the grapes and the wine that came from them, with her own passionate, pagan longings for Marcello.

Last night with only a thin wall between them, sleep had eluded her. Every nerve in her body tingled. Her brain tormented her with vivid recollections of their embraces . . . of their lips meeting . . . of their flesh touching. Gina hungered for that touch . . . and more, for some crumb of assurance that Marcello shared at least part of what she was feeling. But he offered no evidence of that assurance.

Ever since she had told him she meant to marry Quentin, he had treated her as if she were made of glass. Except for those brief moments after the bullfight she had felt as distant from him as if she were still in Alentejo and he were in Lisbon.

Theirs was such a backward romance, she mourned—if indeed it could be called a romance at all. Enviously she watched the fecund harvest moving into full swing while she, on its outskirts, felt barren and wasted. When she and Marcello had known each other only a few days they had been so intensely attracted to each other she had allowed him to open her blouse and kiss her breasts as if she had belonged to him forever. In Isabel's apartment she had thrilled to his hands stroking her flesh. And now, weeks later, they were worlds apart and as withdrawn in their relationship as if they had been introduced only five minutes before.

Of course, it was her fault. All her fault. Marcello was right in his accusation that she kept secrets—even from herself—that she was afraid of her own emotions. She was beginning to see at last that her father was not entirely to blame for the failure of his marriage. Her mother, whom she had never been able to view objectively before, had been clinging, utterly dependent . . . on Gina as well as upon her husband. That must have galled Christian Thomas. He was a debonair man married to a woman who had never wanted to step out of the house. No wonder they had made each other so miserable.

Looking at herself through Marcello's eyes, Gina saw that the uncertainty of her home life had made her shy away from emotional risk. And she was bigoted, too—as bigoted as Emilio! Just as blindly as her uncle, she had stereotyped Marcello in a role he could not remotely fill. Blinded by the image of her father that she had superimposed upon him, she had failed to see that he possessed a complex personality like no other man and could not possibly be categorized.

Marcello found her flushed and nervous when he returned to the car and he scolded her lightly for not having found a spot in the shade to wait for him. Quick tears of self-pity burned at her eyelids. Even in small things, she could not please him!

But her spirits lifted when he announced that the *lagar,* the building that housed the treading vat she was eager to see, was just ahead.

"We can walk if you like."

Marcello himself seemed eager to view the ancient rite of stomping the grapes again, and Gina fell into step beside him with a lighter heart.

"Have you finished your business?" she inquired as they moved through the dappled sunlight.

Marcello nodded. "But my office in Lisbon has tracked me down. There's a problem there that needs my attention. I've decided to leave the car here. We'll fly back from Porto this afternoon."

Gina's heart sank. She had counted on one more day at least for a miracle to occur. Wistfully she murmured, "Perhaps Lisbon has disappeared from the face of the earth. Perhaps every place but this enchanted hillside has vanished forever."

In response to this strange speech, Marcello swung his head around sharply, and she felt his gaze burning through her, but he said nothing and steered her into the cavernous gloom of the *lagar*.

Gina hung back for a moment, but then her eyes accustomed themselves to the shadowy interior of the old building. The indistinct forms she had observed moving about in the bottom of the enormous stone tank were young people, she saw. Couples. The lower part of the vat was filled with grapes, and while an accordionist played melancholy love songs she recognized from the Casa de Fado, the young men and women with their hands upon each other's shoulders moved dreamily through swirling purple juice.

"So this is how it's done!" Gina breathed in the heady fragrance of the grapes excitedly.

"This is a modern version of it," Marcello replied. "Formerly, men marched shoulder to shoulder, but this is more fun and gets the job done just as well . . . better, some people believe, than the new machines which crush the stems and seeds as well as the fruit and give the wine a faintly bitter taste."

Some of the young people who had recognized Marcello began to cry out, "Come down, *senhor!* You and the *senhorita*. Help us!"

Marcello's even white teeth showed in a smile. "I'm afraid we forgot our swimsuits."

An elderly bearded man who had joined them at the edge of the vat remarked, "Pardon, *senhor* Severa, but we can accommodate you if you like. In the dressing rooms there are shorts and shirts."

"Oh, Marcello, could we?" Gina's eyes shone. "I'd like to give it a try!"

For a moment his amused glance moved over her, but then he nodded in assent and they were led away to separate rooms where they could change their clothes.

Within a few minutes Marcello was handing Gina carefully down into the sea of purple. "Be careful," he warned, delighted at her breathless squeals of pleasure. "If you fall, you may find yourself bottled and corked and on your way to Porto."

Gina was quick to agree that the slippery pulp did afford a treacherous footing, and she clung tightly to Marcello's wide shoulders, feeling the same sense of physical release she had experienced making mudpies as a child.

He held her closer. "It's not as easy as it looks, is it?"

"Far from it!" She smiled giddily up at him.

"But it's wonderful. I feel so deliciously wicked!"

Marcello's strong fingers pressed into the flesh of her shoulders. "All we need is Isabel to sing for us."

Gina closed her eyes and swayed in time with the accordion. The music and the fumes of fermentation rising from the grapes flowed together to create an erotic haze, and she began to understand the detached dreaminess she had seen on the faces of the other treaders.

In a few minutes she commented drowsily, "I think we could get drunk just breathing down here. Intoxicating air—think of the market for that in Paris or Rome."

"That's why everyone else is climbing out," Marcello told her in a voice close to her ear. "Periodically the treaders need to clear their lungs."

Reluctantly Gina opened her eyes and saw that what he said was true. The last couple was climbing the ladder. She and Marcello were alone except for the accordionist who discreetly turned away.

Marcello fastened a penetrating gaze on her and inquired thickly, "Do you want to get out, too?"

"Not yet." Prickles of desire raced up her spine. "Do you?"

"No. . . ." Time seemed to stop. Gina's lips parted. Marcello's breathing quickened. Then as if a match had been struck to their reserve, it exploded. Marcello gathered her roughly to him. "Gina . . ."

"Oh, Marcello!"

"I may not be the man of granite your Quentin Bromley is, but . . ."

"Marcello, I lied to you! I'm not going to marry Quentin. I don't want a man of granite."

"Do you want a man who loves you with all of his heart?"

"Yes . . . yes!"

Neither of them noticed that the music had stopped, that the only sounds echoing against the stones were the raspings of their breath.

Between kisses, Marcello muttered hoarsely, "You've been so far away from me for such a long time."

"Never from my thoughts." She clung to him feverishly. "Never for a minute."

They kissed deeply, hungrily, yielding to each other. Marcello almost lost his footing. They tilted crazily . . . then, laughing, their lips met again.

# Chapter Eleven

In the plane, Gina, still starry-eyed, sat close
to Marcello, her hand curled in his, not caring
what the other passengers might think of her
faintly purple legs or of the frankly adoring
glances the two of them were exchanging.

"Is this really happening?" she whispered
once, and Marcello answered huskily, "It's
been happening for weeks. But we were just
too blind to see it."

She snuggled happily against his side.
"You're kind to say 'we' when it was I who was
blind. You are so forgiving, Marcello." She
had already explained her complex feelings
about her parents and the effect they had had
on her life, but now she added, "You were so
right when you said it's how we react to our

problems that matter, that is what makes us who we are."

He kissed her brow tenderly. "I love who you are, and I won't let you take all the blame for keeping us apart. I had reservations of my own to overcome. You seemed half-a-dozen personalities rolled into one. It took me some time to see that this is why you enchant me."

The blue of his eyes deepened. "Your moods are a medley of climates, my darling. Sunshine and showers, thunder and cloudless skies. I look forward to a lifetime of experiencing them all."

Gina sighed and questioned dreamily, "Do you think any other woman ever accepted a proposal of marriage while standing up to her hips in grape juice?"

He kissed her lightly. "Who cares? You did, and you're the only woman who matters to me."

Suddenly, she was serious, hating the chill around her heart. "What about Sylvia?"

He chuckled. "She'll be surprised when she hears our good news."

"Oh, Marcello, I'm afraid she won't be." Gina moistened her lips. "I tried to tell you before we left Lisbon. About my quarrel with Sylvia."

She blurted out the rest in one long breath. "I know this won't make sense—it doesn't to me either—but I told Sylvia that you and I were going to be married, and that we planned to live at Sintra and that she would never be allowed to darken our door."

Marcello gave her an astonished look and then burst out laughing. "You feisty little Yankee!" He squeezed her shoulder. "You had your claws into me deeper than I imagined."

"Don't joke, Marcello! Sylvia was livid. She's set on marrying you herself."

Marcello shook his head. "She isn't, or if she is, she's buried her head in the sand. She and I had all that out ages ago, soon after she arrived in the spring." He went on gruffly, "She wanted us to be lovers. I didn't. Finally we settled on going out together, but with no entanglements, romantic or otherwise."

He saw Gina's frown and teased, "Sylvia can be fascinating company." Then he sobered. "But she's a shallow schemer. I could never take her seriously."

Gina eyed him fearfully. "You've told her that?"

"She forced me to. She was on the verge of ordering the wedding cake."

Then his amusement gave way to a solemn gaze. Cupping Gina's chin, he said quietly, "Sylvia has never been anything more to me than a passing acquaintance with whom I've shared some pleasant evenings." He bent his head and kissed Gina softly. "It's you I love, you I want in my arms for the rest of my life. Can't you believe that?"

Gina let out her breath and laid her head on his shoulder. "I think now I can."

When the plane landed in Lisbon, Gina wanted to go straight to Isabel's. "She's half in love with you herself," she chattered while Marcello claimed their bags. "We can't risk letting her find out from someone else."

But in the backseat of the taxi that Marcello flagged, he kissed Gina until she was limp and then he said in a voice roughened by suppressed ardor, "We can see Isabel later. We're going home first."

"Home?" she said faintly.

He kissed her again, trailing his lips over hers, setting instant fires with their passage. "Home, my darling," he muttered hoarsely, "is wherever we can be together."

"Yes, Marcello." She fitted herself against his warm side. "Yes—take me home."

The ride up in the elevator seemed endless, even with Marcello smothering her with kisses. The hallway leading to his door stretched for miles . . . the key in the lock seemed frozen.

Then at last they were inside. Standing in the entry hall, Marcello took off the sweater that covered her white shirt, he threw her purse aside. He kissed the hollow of her throat and unclasped the gold necklace that hung there.

"Gina . . ." His hot look of love entered her and set off an urgent storm of hungers. He swung her up in his arms just as the doorbell rang.

"We can't just ignore it, can we?" Gina whispered.

"Of course we can."

"But it might be someone from your office, something urgent."

Marcello buried his face in her neck. "Nothing is more urgent than this."

"No, Marcello. At least, let's see who it is!" Reluctantly, she pushed him away and slid to the floor. He unclasped his arms from her shoulders and moved slowly toward the door.

It flashed through Gina's mind the moment she saw Sylvia King that everything was over. Marcello would never make love to Gina. She would never marry him. If a rabbit's foot and a four-leaf clover symbolized luck, and rainbows equaled happiness, there were omens for evil as well—the Sylvia Kings of the world who had the power to reduce blazing fires to ashes.

"What do you want?" asked Marcello bluntly.

Sylvia swept past, her pale eyes raking Gina's tense form. "Obviously, Marcello, this woman's bad manners have rubbed off on you."

"This woman," he said with deadly calm, "is going to be my wife."

"So I've heard." Sylvia turned slowly, letting her gaze drift to the chair where Gina's sweater lay with her purse and the gold chain that dangled over the arm. "Have I interrupted something?"

"What do you want?" Marcello repeated, his hand still on the doorknob.

Sylvia opened her own purse and took out a folded slip of paper which she passed across in front of Gina. "I want to give this to you."

Marcello took it. "What is it?"

"Read it," said Sylvia languidly. "I hope you'll be as delighted as I am."

At her side, Gina felt Marcello grow rigid. "What kind of nonsense is this?" he snorted.

"It's not nonsense. Just good news . . . in a few months you'll be a father."

Marcello roared at her, "Get out of here, Sylvia!"

Arched brows lifted. "Oh, my . . . there's your Spanish mother's temper."

*Marcello a father? Of Sylvia's baby?* The words burned in Gina's brain. She heard Marcello's strident voice lashing out at Sylvia's accusations, but his angry denial failed to reach her. She was only aware of Sylvia's self-satisfied smile as the other woman turned to leave.

"You may shout all you want, darling, in cool contempt, I'll win. You'll see. I always do," Sylvia said as Marcello closed the door behind her.

"What rubbish!" exploded Marcello. "What colossal rubbish!" He reached again for Gina, but she drew back. Hardly aware of what she was doing, she groped for her sweater on the chair behind her and began to put it on.

Scowling, Marcello watched her. "Gina! What on earth are you doing?"

Pale and tight-lipped, Gina fastened the clasp on her necklace.

"Gina! Where are you going?"

"You told me you hadn't made love to Sylvia."

"That's right." He stopped in front of her, arms folded across his wide chest.

Gina retorted swiftly, "Not recently, perhaps."

"Not ever."

His gaze was so steady, his voice so sure that for an instant Gina almost relented. But logic intervened swiftly. Sylvia was vengeful, but not stupid. She would never accuse a man she hadn't slept with of being the father of her child.

"I don't believe you."

Marcello's whole expression hardened. "Obviously."

"I know you . . . I know your passion." Gina was trembling from head to foot. "Sylvia is a beautiful woman, and a willing one!"

"Does that mean that two and two add up to five?" He caught hold of her shoulders and said harshly. "You've behaved like a child long enough! Listen to me. I learned long ago not to mix intimately with Sylvia's kind. Whatever they touch, they taint."

"I see, and did you learn that noble lesson from fathering some other unfortunate child you're not man enough to claim?"

Marcello let go of her with a suddenness that sent her reeling back against the chair.

"Thank you for saying that." His voice honed to a razor sharpness that matched the steel in his eyes. "You and I were on the verge of making the mistake of our lives. Thank you for saving us."

Through a blur of tears, Gina snatched up her purse. "Sylvia saved us. You can thank her, in any way you please!"

Gina took a taxi to Isabel's apartment, but not until she was paying the driver did she remember that her bags were still at Marcello's. She thought of sending the cabman back for them, but even that small effort required more of her than she could manage. Dismissing him, she stumbled up the stairs. What if Isabel were still away? she thought desperately.

But from inside the apartment she heard Isabel's voice raised in argument. She paused before the open door, dreading an encounter with Claudio, but in a moment Isabel emerged from the bedroom carrying on a heated monologue with herself.

When she caught sight of Gina, she shrieked joyfully, "My darling American cousin, is it you?"

Rushing forward, she exclaimed, "Where have you been? Are you all right? You look pale!"

Gina smiled feebly and allowed herself to be led to a chair. "I'm all right, just tired. I took a short trip up the coast." She ran the tip of her tongue over her parched lips. "If you've been worried, I'm sorry."

Isabel rolled her eyes. "Worried! If you had

not come back today, I would have called the police!"

"Emilio and Valentina . . . ?"

"Do not upset yourself. I did tell them you were missing. Have you been with Marcello?" She peered at Gina, avid for details. When Gina only nodded, she said with a wise lift of her eyebrows, "Ah, since you are here and he is not you must have quarreled."

"Yes."

Isabel's sigh was like a tongue of fire blazing forth. "You quarreled with Marcello—and *I* could strangle Claudio!"

"Isabel!"

"Not in truth," Isabel said regretfully. "Only in thought. How can I wring his scrawny neck when he is sulking with his Mama in Venice?"

"Venice?" Gina was bewildered. "What happened? What went wrong?"

Isabel stretched dramatically on the couch, but almost at once she was upright again, leaning forward, glaring at Gina.

"Do you know who has come knocking here on two days before yesterday? Mrs. America. Mrs. Sylvia King."

A wave of nausea struck Gina. So a black shadow had passed over the whole city of Lisbon! "What did she want?"

"She wanted Claudio!"

"Claudio?"

Isabel sat back. "Mrs. Sylvia King . . ." she paused for effect, "is Claudio's mistress."

171

"What?"

Black eyes snapped in Isabel's flushed face. "Is that not cause enough for strangling him? While I gave my heart and soul to Claudio, Sylvia King gave him everything else!"

"But that's ridiculous." Gina felt as if a club had struck her. "Claudio doesn't even like her."

"Like has nothing to do with it, my poor innocent. For months they have been slipping off to Sylvia's dove nest in Estoril and making love while I am sleeping with my hands folded like an angel all alone in my bed, except when you are here."

"I don't understand this."

"You do not know the biggest fact of all . . . Mrs. King is having Claudio's baby!"

Isabel greeted Gina's open-mouthed stare with a grim smile of affirmation. "I am like you, my darling Gina—the wind is knocked out of me. But whether we believe it or not, it is true. Claudio told me so himself."

"Sylvia is having Claudio's baby?"

"Unless she decides not to have it," said Isabel darkly. Then, observing Gina's pallor, she said soothingly, "It is all so complicated, we will forget about it and speak of the coast." She stretched her lips in a bright smile. "Tell me, how was the weather?"

Gina all but shrieked. "Isabel! I have to know everything—from the very beginning!"

"You will faint."

"I will not faint!"

Reluctantly, Isabel took her place again on

the couch. "On Sunday I was sitting here in a state of nervousness because I couldn't think how to explain to Father and Mama that I was not going to live in Alfama anymore, and that I planned to be the *fadista* in London, in Paris, in Vienna."

"What?"

"No interruptions, please! If you stop me, I will get mixed up. I was sitting here when Claudio arrived. He said he would take me to Estoril to cheer me up, but I could soon see he was planning this vacation before he even knew that I needed my spirits lifted. For one thing, he gave me flowers he had already picked and he was taking me out on his terrace where dinner was waiting."

Suddenly her voice dropped and lost its drama. "Claudio gave me a ring, Gina. He asked me to be the *senhora* Countess Medoc."

"Claudio asked you to *marry* him?"

"Yes . . . me. Isabel from Alentejo." Her eyes brimmed with sudden tears. "It was a very large diamond he slipped on my finger. The sparkles lit up the terrace." She sniffed woefully. "But I told Claudio 'no.' I took off his ring and put it back in the box."

"Why? You didn't know about Sylvia then, did you? Why did you turn him down?"

"In my life there are two things I want," said Isabel. "One is to be the Countess Medoc, and the other is to be the *fadista* all of Europe knows. But I found out I wanted to be the *fadista* more than I wanted to be the countess. That morning before Claudio came to

173

take me to Estoril, the telegram had arrived from the men who heard me sing at Sylvia's."

Isabel brought the wire out of a pocket in her dressing gown and smoothed it out on the table. "Tomorrow I leave for Paris."

"Oh, Isabel!" Gina's eyes skipped over the words that made up the long-awaited offer. For a moment everything else was forgotten. "How wonderful for you!" How fortunate, too, Gina thought. Even if behind Isabel's back, Claudio had not taken Sylvia for a lover, he would have made Isabel an unfaithful husband.

"Wonderful, yes," said Isabel, angry again all at once. "But Claudio would not allow me to enjoy it. He was like a bee stinging me in the ear. All that evening and all the next day he was telling me how much better it was to be a countess. Then finally he went down on his knees and said I could be the countess and the *fadista* too, even though he knew that could never be."

"Why not?" said Gina, though she was fearful of tipping the balance back in Claudio's favor.

But Isabel was reconciled. "If there is too much happiness in the *fadista's* life," she answered firmly, "she cannot be sad enough to sing fado. So I must make this sacrifice for my career."

Her eyes blazed again. "Now I will be the greatest *fadista* in all the world because of what Claudio and Sylvia have done. Because I am so wronged in love!"

"Sylvia actually came here and told you that she and Claudio were lovers?"

"Ha!" Isabel scoffed. "She would not dare. She knows I would kill her! She only told me with her cat's smile that I should tell Claudio she had a message for him. That it was not the same message she gave him the first time. I slammed the door in her face and I called Claudio to say that the next time Mrs. King comes to my place asking for him, I will shoot her and then I'll shoot him! This is when I found out that he had left for Venice."

Isabel smirked. "Poor, broken-hearted Claudio, I was thinking. He has gone home to cry in his mama's lap because I will not marry him. But no! This was not the case at all. When I rang him up in Venice, I teased him a little, and told him I was sending him Sylvia King by mail, who was searching for him to discuss urgent matters." Isabel's black brows climbed her forehead. "Do you know what, my darling Gina? When I told him this, the truth came flying out."

Her expression darkened ominously. "I found out that Claudio didn't even want to marry me. He only asked me to spite Sylvia. She was spiting Marcello because Marcello would never make love to her."

"What, Isabel? Wait!"

Isabel shot her a fierce look. "I warned you before we started that this was complicated. Don't you dare faint!"

"Of course I won't faint. But you're not making sense."

"How can you say that when I haven't told you everything yet? You can't realize how angry Sylvia was when I told her that you and Marcello were getting married." Isabel paused. "This was before your quarrel, right?"

"Right! Go on!"

"Mrs. America King hates Marcello for treating her so coldly and you so warmly. When Claudio made up his mind to marry her since she was having his baby, and he wanted to, she said to him, 'Not yet, darling Claudio. First I am going to tell Marcello the baby is his, to watch him squirm.'"

"That's what I'm saying, Isabel!" cried Gina. "If Marcello and Sylvia were never . . ."

"Wait!" Isabel said excitedly. "Claudio was furious and told her he would not wait five minutes for an ungrateful woman to whom he was offering his seven-hundred year-old name. He decided to marry me, instead—with the same ring and flowers!" Fires of triumph lit Isabel's eyes. "But I said 'no,' too! Two rejections in one day!" she crowed. "This is when Count Medoc crawled home to his mama!"

Gina had no sympathy to spare for Claudio. "If it were true that Marcello never made love to Sylvia, what would be the point in Sylvia's telling him that he's the father of her child? He would know, of course that he couldn't be!"

"The point, my darling cousin, is that Mrs. America King hoped to spoil Marcello's happiness with her announcement. She felt that *you* would believe what she said. That you would quarrel with Marcello and call off the wedding."

Her gaze riveted to Gina's and for an instant they stared at each other.

"Good heavens," said Isabel, for once stunned to a whisper. "You have already done that, haven't you? Oh, Gina, you must go to Marcello at once!"

"It's too late. Oh, Isabel, it's too late! I said terrible things. Marcello could never forgive me."

"But if you do not go to him, then Sylvia King wins!"

Gina covered her face with her hands. "She warned Marcello that she would. She said she always does."

# Chapter Twelve

Up to the last minute before Isabel stepped onto her plane for Paris, she was still begging Gina to go to Marcello. But Gina was even firmer in the morning light than she had been the evening before.

"Marcello and I had something beautiful, but it was too fragile," she told Isabel with a tearful hug. "I took a sledge hammer to a soap bubble. We could never put it back together again."

"You could try!" wailed Isabel.

"And risk breaking my heart all over again? No thanks. Goodbye, Isabel. Come to see me on Nantucket when you've finished knocking everyone cold in the watering spots of Europe."

Gina kept her smile until the plane took off. She took a taxi back to the apartment that she had promised Isabel she would close before going to Alentejo to bid goodby to Emilio and Valentina. Isabel's car was already in storage, so that was taken care of. There were a few potted plants to give to a neighbor and the key to leave with the landlady, and then she could be off.

Sometime during the long, sleepless night, she had decided that nothing in her bags, which were still at Marcello's, was important enough for her to risk making contact with him again. She had to worry about only the clothes on her back, her passport, and the plane ticket in her purse.

Travel light, she told herself grimly. Wasn't that what everyone always advised? But on her way down the stairs with the potted plants, she decided she needed at least one change of clothes. Something from Isabel's closet that she could send back before it was missed.

Setting the pots on the landing, she went back up, leaving the door open behind her. In a few minutes she emerged from the bedroom with a skirt and blouse tucked into her over-sized handbag.

Marcello was standing in the living room.

"You left these," he said when he saw her, and set her bags down on the rug.

She had never seen him look ashen be-

179

fore . . . or was she only seeing herself reflected in his eyes? "Yes." She moistened her lips. "Thank you."

"Were you on your way out?"

"I'm going to Alentejo." Her blood thundered against her eardrums. "I'm saying goodbye. I've updated my ticket. I'm leaving at the end of the week."

"I see. Then I came just in time, didn't I?"

No, my darling, she longed to cry out. You're much too late. But she only nodded.

"Isabel's gone," she added irrelevantly. "But I guess you already know about that."

"About what?"

"Your friends have hired her. She left for Paris this morning."

"Good for Isabel."

His voice sounded so flat, so disinterested in a cause he had championed that Gina felt a twinge of alarm overriding her pain. Perhaps he was ill. Perhaps she should ask him to sit down . . . offer him water . . . or a glass of port. Instead she said, "Claudio asked her to marry him."

"Isabel?" Marcello made a sound that was not quite a laugh.

"She turned him down, and he ran off to Venice. He only asked her to spite Sylvia."

Marcello's jaw hardened. "You've learned quite a lot since I saw you last."

"Yes, I have." Her heart had gone wild inside her chest . . . but it wasn't breaking! It felt, in fact, more itself than it had since yesterday. Fate had given her one more chance. If only she could make good use of it! "I've learned that Sylvia and Claudio are lovers. That the child she expects is his, that I accused you unjustly."

If only he would stop staring at her!

She went on recklessly. "I see now what I should have seen all along . . . what Isabel should have seen too. Claudio dropped so many clues. He was so eager to match up you and me so that he could have a clear field with Sylvia. He knew in advance more about her party than he had any right to. He was furious that Sylvia had dealt behind his back by arranging it for Isabel because you asked her to."

Gina paused. "But you knew all along, didn't you? I remember once you said that Claudio thrived on complications."

"His back was against the wall. He had no choice," Marcello said bluntly. "He was living on the last of his inheritance. He was counting on Sylvia's fortune to replenish the dregs in his bank account."

"How do you know?" said Gina, shocked.

"Sylvia told me." A grim smile of irony twisted Marcello's lips. "Your Nantucket background was not the only one she researched."

"Isabel has no money," Gina protested. "If he was desperate, why did he want to marry her?"

"The next best thing to fortune is fame," Marcello replied. "And besides, I think in his own way, Claudio did care for Isabel. It's too bad for him that she didn't say yes. If anyone could have, she would have made a man of him."

Tears blurred Gina's vision. For the first time she understood the true meaning of *sua-dade*, the longing for what might have been that haunted Isabel's songs. If only she could roll back time. If this were Marcello's apartment instead of Isabel's, and the doorbell rang, she would never allow him to answer it. If she hadn't been so stubborn . . . if she had trusted Marcello as he deserved.

Love did have two faces—rapture and sorrow. At the Casa de Fado, Isabel had said, *it is not possible to separate them . . . the bitter and the sweet mingle . . . that is life . . . that is what I sing about. . . .*

But why was there so much that was bitter and so little that was sweet?

She gazed sorrowfully down at her bags. There was nothing left for her to do but go. "Thank you for bringing these," she murmured again.

"What would you have done if I hadn't?"

The challenge she heard in Marcello's voice made her look up quickly. She saw that the coppery glow had returned to his skin. In his blue eyes there was actually a stern twinkle.

He came toward her. "You would have gone off and left them, wouldn't you, you little idiot? You'd have run off like Claudio rather than face me."

If it was pride that had kept her from him, she had no use for it now.

"Oh, Marcello . . ." She was weeping openly. "I didn't want to run away from you! I wanted to come running back the minute I heard the truth."

"From someone else, you mean," he said sardonically. "You had already heard it once from me."

"But that's just it, don't you see? How could I come back and expect you to forgive me when I'd believed someone else and I hadn't believed you? When I'd been so foolish and so faithless . . ."

"And so crazily complicated that I'll never be sure what you're going to do next." All at once he opened his arms and pulled her to him.

"Do you know how special that makes you, my darling?" he said thickly. "Did you really believe for a moment that I'd ever let you get away from me?"

"You want me to stay?" She drew back and searched his face. "Are you saying that you still want to marry me?"

"Do birds fly? Do fishermen fish?"

His mouth covered hers. In a joyous burst of passion, she wrapped her arms around his neck and gave herself to his kiss. She was dreaming, of course . . . these weren't really his hands moving over her skin, his hips thrusting into hers.

Then he was murmuring hotly in her ear, "Do you know what you put me through, walking out on me like that?"

"It was such a stupid quarrel."

"We could have thrown away so much."

He kissed away her tears. He smoothed back her hair and kissed her forehead and her closed eyelids, her throat and the hollow of her shoulder.

"I love you, Marcello." How delicious those words tasted! "I love you."

Marcello held her face gently between his hands and touched her lips with his. "Don't ever be afraid again that I'll hurt you, Gina."

"No." This was Marcello's chest, this was his heart beating steadily beneath her ear. "You're not like my father. You're not like anyone except yourself. Oh, Marcello . . ." She pulled back to gaze at him. "Five minutes ago I thought my world was ending—now I know it's just beginning." The radiance of her smile broke through the last traces of her tears. "What shall we do first?"

"First?" he questioned solemnly. He studied her for a long minute, pulling his thumb slowly across her lips. "First go into the bedroom and put on that silky thing."

Her heart stopped. "My robe?"

"No." His blue eyes twinkled. "The dress you had on the night we met. That's what I want you to be wearing when I ask Emilio for your hand."

"Emilio!"

"He's next of kin. You want to abide by custom, don't you?"

"He'll never say yes."

"He'd better not say no!"

They kissed again. "Perhaps," said Marcel-

184

lo hoarsely, "putting on your robe is a better idea after all."

"You missed your chance," Gina teased and slipped out of his embrace. "Anyway, I like the first plan. Once you've committed yourself to Emilio you won't dare back out or he'll have your head."

"If he does that will be twice in twenty-four hours."

"What do you mean?"

"After you left yesterday, your Mr. Bromley called."

"Quentin called *you*?" Gina gazed at him in stunned disbelief. "What on earth for?"

"Sylvia had set a fire under him. He was ready to come with the Massachusetts militia and hang me up by my thumbs for seducing his sweetheart."

All the breath left Gina. "I can't believe this!"

"You will when you call him, and you have to. I promised."

"What did Sylvia tell him?"

"Enough for him to come to rescue you. He leaves at six this evening, unless you stop him." Marcello took her in his arms again and whispered along her cheekbone, "He cares very much for you. Are you sure you don't want to change your mind and go back to America with him?"

"I might." She bit the end of Marcello's nose. "You may have suffered a little, but you've known since yesterday that we were still going to get married."

He bit her earlobe in return. "I've known a lot longer than that. I've gradually been getting used to the idea since the day I kissed you at the Castle of St. George."

Gina's mouth flew open. "You've taken your sweet time telling me!"

"Why not?" He ran a finger down her cheek. "You can't blame a man for resenting it a little when a peacock tells him who his wife will be."

# IT'S YOUR OWN SPECIAL TIME

*Contemporary romances for today's women.
Each month, six very special love stories will be yours
from SILHOUETTE. Look for them wherever books are sold
or order now from the coupon below.*

## $1.50 each

| | | | |
|---|---|---|---|
| ☐ 5 Goforth | ☐ 28 Hampson | ☐ 54 Beckman | ☐ 83 Halston |
| ☐ 6 Stanford | ☐ 29 Wildman | ☐ 55 LaDame | ☐ 84 Vitek |
| ☐ 7 Lewis | ☐ 30 Dixon | ☐ 56 Trent | ☐ 85 John |
| ☐ 8 Beckman | ☐ 32 Michaels | ☐ 57 John | ☐ 86 Adams |
| ☐ 9 Wilson | ☐ 33 Vitek | ☐ 58 Stanford | ☐ 87 Michaels |
| ☐ 10 Caine | ☐ 34 John | ☐ 59 Vernon | ☐ 88 Stanford |
| ☐ 11 Vernon | ☐ 35 Stanford | ☐ 60 Hill | ☐ 89 James |
| ☐ 17 John | ☐ 38 Browning | ☐ 61 Michaels | ☐ 90 Major |
| ☐ 19 Thornton | ☐ 39 Sinclair | ☐ 62 Halston | ☐ 92 McKay |
| ☐ 20 Fulford | ☐ 46 Stanford | ☐ 63 Brent | ☐ 93 Browning |
| ☐ 22 Stephens | ☐ 47 Vitek | ☐ 71 Ripy | ☐ 94 Hampson |
| ☐ 23 Edwards | ☐ 48 Wildman | ☐ 73 Browning | ☐ 95 Wisdom |
| ☐ 24 Healy | ☐ 49 Wisdom | ☐ 76 Hardy | ☐ 96 Beckman |
| ☐ 25 Stanford | ☐ 50 Scott | ☐ 78 Oliver | ☐ 97 Clay |
| ☐ 26 Hastings | ☐ 52 Hampson | ☐ 81 Roberts | ☐ 98 St. George |
| ☐ 27 Hampson | ☐ 53 Browning | ☐ 82 Dailey | ☐ 99 Camp |

## $1.75 each

| | | | |
|---|---|---|---|
| ☐ 100 Stanford | ☐ 110 Trent | ☐ 120 Carroll | ☐ 130 Hardy |
| ☐ 101 Hardy | ☐ 111 South | ☐ 121 Langan | ☐ 131 Stanford |
| ☐ 102 Hastings | ☐ 112 Stanford | ☐ 122 Scofield | ☐ 132 Wisdom |
| ☐ 103 Cork | ☐ 113 Browning | ☐ 123 Sinclair | ☐ 133 Rowe |
| ☐ 104 Vitek | ☐ 114 Michaels | ☐ 124 Beckman | ☐ 134 Charles |
| ☐ 105 Eden | ☐ 115 John | ☐ 125 Bright | ☐ 135 Logan |
| ☐ 106 Dailey | ☐ 116 Lindley | ☐ 126 St. George | ☐ 136 Hampson |
| ☐ 107 Bright | ☐ 117 Scott | ☐ 127 Roberts | ☐ 137 Hunter |
| ☐ 108 Hampson | ☐ 118 Dailey | ☐ 128 Hampson | ☐ 138 Wilson |
| ☐ 109 Vernon | ☐ 119 Hampson | ☐ 129 Converse | ☐ 139 Vitek |

## $1.75 each

| | | | |
|---|---|---|---|
| ☐ 140 Erskine | ☐ 160 Hampson | ☐ 179 Beckman | ☐ 198 Hunter |
| ☐ 142 Browning | ☐ 161 Trent | ☐ 180 Roberts | ☐ 199 Roberts |
| ☐ 143 Roberts | ☐ 162 Ashby | ☐ 181 Terrill | ☐ 200 Lloyd |
| ☐ 144 Goforth | ☐ 163 Roberts | ☐ 182 Clay | ☐ 201 Starr |
| ☐ 145 Hope | ☐ 164 Browning | ☐ 183 Stanley | ☐ 202 Hampson |
| ☐ 146 Michaels | ☐ 165 Young | ☐ 184 Hardy | ☐ 203 Browning |
| ☐ 147 Hampson | ☐ 166 Wisdom | ☐ 185 Hampson | ☐ 204 Carroll |
| ☐ 148 Cork | ☐ 167 Hunter | ☐ 186 Howard | ☐ 205 Maxam |
| ☐ 149 Saunders | ☐ 168 Carr | ☐ 187 Scott | ☐ 206 Manning |
| ☐ 150 Major | ☐ 169 Scott | ☐ 188 Cork | ☐ 207 Windham |
| ☐ 151 Hampson | ☐ 170 Ripy | ☐ 189 Stephens | ☐ 208 Halston |
| ☐ 152 Halston | ☐ 171 Hill | ☐ 190 Hampson | ☐ 209 LaDame |
| ☐ 153 Dailey | ☐ 172 Browning | ☐ 191 Browning | ☐ 210 Eden |
| ☐ 154 Beckman | ☐ 173 Camp | ☐ 192 John | ☐ 211 Walters |
| ☐ 155 Hampson | ☐ 174 Sinclair | ☐ 193 Trent | ☐ 212 Young |
| ☐ 156 Sawyer | ☐ 175 Jarrett | ☐ 194 Barry | ☐ 213 Dailey |
| ☐ 157 Vitek | ☐ 176 Vitek | ☐ 195 Dailey | |
| ☐ 158 Reynolds | ☐ 177 Dailey | ☐ 196 Hampson | |
| ☐ 159 Tracy | ☐ 178 Hampson | ☐ 197 Summers | |

## $1.95 each

| | |
|---|---|
| __#214 LOVE SO RARE Hampson | __#220 THE DAWN IS GOLDEN, Hampson |
| __#215 HER MOTHER'S KEEPER Roberts | __#221 PRACTICAL DREAMER, Browning |
| __#216 LOVE'S SWEET MUSIC Saunders | __#222 TWO FACES OF LOVE, Carroll |
| __#217 BLUE MIST OF MORNING Vitek | __#223 A PRIVATE EDEN, Summers |
| __#218 FOUNTAINS OF PARADISE Hunter | __#224 HIDDEN ISLE, Langan |
| __#219 ISLAND SPELL Cork | __#225 DELTA RIVER MAGIC, St. George |

## Look for _LOST IN LOVE_ by Mia Maxam available in July.

**SILHOUETTE BOOKS,** Department SB/1
1230 Avenue of the Americas
New York, NY 10020

Please send me the books I have checked above. I am enclosing $_____
(please add 50¢ to cover postage and handling. NYS and NYC residents please
add appropriate sales tax). Send check or money order—no cash or C.O.D.'s
please. Allow six weeks for delivery.

NAME _____

ADDRESS _____

CITY _____ STATE/ZIP _____

*Silhouette* **Romance**

# 15-Day Free Trial Offer
# 6 Silhouette Romances

**6 Silhouette Romances, free for 15 days!** We'll send you 6 new Silhouette Romances to keep for 15 days, absolutely free! If you decide not to keep them, send them back to us. You pay nothing.

**Free Home Delivery.** But if you enjoy them as much as we think you will, keep them by paying the invoice enclosed with your free trial shipment. We'll pay all shipping and handling charges. You get the convenience of Home Delivery and we pay the postage and handling charge each month.

**Don't miss a copy.** The Silhouette Book Club is the way to make sure you'll be able to receive every new romance we publish before they're sold out. There is no minimum number of books to buy and you can cancel at any time.

This offer expires November 30, 1983

Silhouette Book Club, Dept. **SRSR7A**
120 Brighton Road, Clifton, NJ 07012

Please send me 6 Silhouette Romances to keep for 15 days, absolutely free. I understand I am not obligated to join the Silhouette Book Club unless I decide to keep them.

NAME_____

ADDRESS_____

CITY_____STATE_____ZIP_____

# Get the Silhouette Books Newsletter every month for a year.

Now you can receive the fascinating and informative Silhouette Books Newsletter 12 times a year. Every issue is packed with inside information about your favorite Silhouette authors, upcoming books, and a variety of entertaining features— including the authors' favorite romantic recipes, quizzes on plots and characters, and articles about the locales featured in Silhouette books. Plus contests where you can win terrific prizes.

The Silhouette Books Newsletter has been available only to Silhouette Home Subscribers. Now you, too, can enjoy the Newsletter all year long for just $19.95. Enter your subscription now, so you won't miss a single exciting issue.

*Silhouette Books*

Send your name and address with check or money order, payable to S & S Enterprises, for $19.95 per subscription, to Simon & Schuster Enterprises, Silhouette Newsletter, 1230 Avenue of the Americas, New York, NY 10020.

New York residents add appropriate sales tax.